Principles of Bookkeeping Controls

Workbook

David Cox
Michael Fardon

Published by Osborne Books Limited
Tel 01905 748071
Email books@osbornebooks.co.uk
Website www.osbornebooks.co.uk

Design by Laura Ingham

Printed by CPI Group (UK) Limited, Croydon, CR0 4YY, on environmentally friendly, acid-free paper from managed forests.

British Library Cataloguing in Publication Data
A catalogue record for this book is available from the British Library

ISBN 978-1-911198-53-6

Contents

Introduction

Chapter activities

Answers to chapter activities

Practice assessments – tasks

Answers to practice assessments

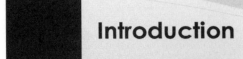

Introduction

Qualifications covered

This book has been written specifically to cover the Unit 'Principles of Bookkeeping Controls' which is mandatory for the following qualifications:

AAT Level 2 Certificate in Accounting

AAT Level 2 Certificate in Bookkeeping

AAT Certificate in Accounting – SCQF Level 6

This book contains Chapter Activities which provide extra practice material in addition to the activities included in the Osborne Books Tutorial text, and Practice Assessments to prepare the student for the computer based assessments. The latter are based directly on the structure, style and content of the sample assessment material provided by the AAT at www.aat.org.uk.

Suggested answers to the Chapter Activities and Practice Assessments are set out in this book.

Osborne Study and Revision Materials

Additional materials, tailored to the needs of students studying this unit and revising for the assessment, include:

- **Tutorials:** paperback books with practice activities
- **Wise Guides:** pocket-sized spiral bound revision cards
- **Student Zone:** access to Osborne Books online resources
- **Osborne Books App:** Osborne Books ebooks for mobiles and tablets

Visit www.osbornebooks.co.uk for details of study and revision resources and access to online material.

Chapter
activities

1 Payment methods

1.1 Cash may be used as a form of payment in which **two** of the following situations?

(a)	Employee wages	
(b)	BACS transfers	
(c)	The petty cash system	
(d)	Payment using Chip and PIN	

1.2 If you are asked to make a payment by post, you are most likely to use which **one** of the following methods?

(a)	CHAPS	
(b)	Cheque	
(c)	Direct debit	
(d)	'Tap and go' debit card	

1.3 Draw lines connecting the four methods of payment listed on the left with the correct descriptions in the boxes on the right.

| debit card |

| enables the card holder to make payment on a monthly basis |

| direct debit |

| takes the payment direct from the customer's bank account |

| standing order |

| regular (fixed date, same amount) payments set up with the bank by the business sending the money |

| credit card |

| variable date and amount BACS payments, set up by the business receiving the payments through its bank |

1.4 For a cheque to be a valid method of payment it has to comply with certain conditions. Indicate in the table below whether the following statements are true or false.

Statement		True	False
(a)	A cheque has to be dated within seven days of making the payment		
(b)	A cheque has to be signed by the person making payment		
(c)	A cheque has to be signed by the person paying it into the bank		
(d)	A cheque has to be paid in within a month of the date written on the top of the cheque		

1.5   Complete the text below by using the appropriate words from the following list:

standing order   **direct debit**

receiver's bank   **variable amounts**

payer's bank

A [   ] is set up by the [   ] and
used to make fixed date payments for the same amount through the banking system.

A [   ] enables [   ]
to be taken from the payer's account and the payments are deducted through the

[   ] .

1.6   You are running a business and have just signed a lease on a rented office. You are incurring various expenses in connection with the office. Which method of payment from the list provided at the end of the question would you choose as the best to use in the situations listed below? Enter the number of the most appropriate payment option in the table below.

		Option number
(a)	Paying rent for the office at a fixed amount of £750 a month	
(b)	Paying insurance premium of £2,000 which increases every year	
(c)	Buying office furniture for £1,200 from a local superstore	
(d)	Paying solicitors fees of £500 plus VAT in connection with lease	
(e)	Buying a travel card for £30 at the local railway station	

List of payment options – enter the option number in the appropriate box in the table above.

1   'tap and go' debit card

2   business credit card

3   direct debit

4   Faster Payment

5   standing order

1.7 You work in the accounts department of J M Supplies Ltd and check payments received from customers. The payments include cheques.

(a) You are to identify **three** errors on the cheque shown below. Write down the errors in the table below.

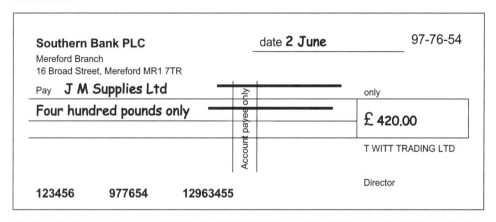

Southern Bank PLC   date **2 June**   97-76-54

Mereford Branch
16 Broad Street, Mereford MR1 7TR

Pay   **J M Supplies Ltd**   only

Four hundred pounds only

Account payee only

£ 420.00

T WITT TRADING LTD

Director

123456   977654   12963455

Error 1	
Error 2	
Error 3	

(b) What action would you take when you had discovered the errors?

(a)	Correct the errors yourself and pay the cheque into the bank	
(b)	Contact T Witt Trading Ltd and ask for a new cheque to be issued	
(c)	Pay the cheque into the bank and hope that the errors will not be noticed	

1.8   Select the most appropriate payment method for each of the following descriptions:

Description	Payment method
An instruction in writing signed by the bank's customer telling the bank to pay a one-off amount to a named person	
A card issued on a 'buy now and pay later' basis; payment is made monthly in full or in part	
A variable date and amount payment, set up by the business receiving the payments	
A paper-based document issued by a bank and used for high value payments	

Choose from the following payment methods – do not use each more than once:

- BACS
- Bank draft
- Cash
- CHAPS
- Cheque
- Credit card
- Debit card
- Direct debit
- Standing order

2 Payment methods and the bank account balance

2.1 Money paid into the bank account of a business earlier rather than later improves which **three** of the following options?

(a)	The solvency of the business	
(b)	The amount of VAT payable to HM Revenue & Customs (HMRC)	
(c)	The reputation of the business in the community	
(d)	Keeping bank charges to a minimum	
(e)	Keeping interest on overdrafts to a minimum	

2.2 Good practice in the management of the bank account of a business should involve which **three** of the following options?

(a)	Keeping the bank account in credit whenever possible	
(b)	Paying in cheques received as late as possible	
(c)	Encouraging customers to pay by Faster Payment	
(d)	Paying wages in cash rather than by BACS credit	
(e)	Paying the business insurance costs by monthly standing order rather than in one payment at the beginning of the period of insurance	

2.3   It is important to appreciate that a 'credit balance' and a 'debit balance' mean opposite things when used by:

(a)   a business describing the bank account in its cash book

(b)   its bank describing the account held by the business and as shown on the bank statement from the bank

Complete the table below indicating in the column on the right whether the situation will result in a debit or credit entry.

Situation	Debit or Credit?
(a) A receipt paid **into** the bank account as shown in the cash book of the business	
(b) A receipt paid **into** the bank account as shown on the bank statement	
(c) A payment **out of** the bank account as shown in the cash book of the business	
(d) A payment **out of** the bank account as shown on the bank statement	

2.4   Which **three** of the payment methods below will **reduce** the balance of the payer's bank account on the day that the payment is made?

Tick the appropriate options.

(a)	Faster Payment	
(b)	Cheque posted to a supplier	
(c)	CHAPS	
(d)	Bank draft	
(e)	Credit card	

2.5 Which **two** of the payment methods listed below will **not reduce** the balance of the payer's bank account on the day that the payment is made?

Tick the appropriate options.

(a)	Cheque paid in at a different bank	
(b)	Bank draft	
(c)	Cash wages	
(d)	Credit card	
(e)	Standing order	

2.6 Draw lines connecting the four methods of payment listed on the left with the appropriate period of time it will normally take for the amount to be deducted from the bank account of the payer.

cash withdrawal

faster payment

CHAPS

cheque sent by post

Amount deducted from the bank account on the same day

Amount deducted from the bank account several days later

2.7   A business receives an invoice from a supplier. The invoice terms are payment within 30 days of the invoice date. There is no prompt payment discount offered. The invoice includes the bank account details of the supplier and payment by electronic transfer is requested.

In order to keep the bank account balance as high as it can for as long as possible, the business will adopt its normal practice and pay the invoice by Faster Payment.

Which **one** of the three options shown below should the business choose to pay the invoice?

(a)	Pay the invoice in the week after it has been received	
(b)	Pay the invoice so that it reaches the supplier's bank as late as possible within the 30 day period	
(c)	Pay the invoice as soon as a chaser for non-payment is received from the supplier after the 30 day period has elapsed	

2.8   **(a)**   Identify which **one** of the following statements is true.

Statement	
It is good practice to pay cheques received during the month into the bank account at the end of the month	
A bank overdraft should be arranged in advance of being required	
A bank does not make a charge when it has to return unpaid cheques that its customer has issued	

(b)   Identify whether each of the following statements is true or false.

Statement	True	False
A cheque paid in at a different bank or branch from the cheque issuer will be deducted from the issuer's account one working day later		
A payment made by debit card is normally deducted from the bank account on the same working day		
A CHAPS electronic bank transfer is deducted from the sender's bank account on the day that the transfer is made		

3   Bank reconciliation statements

3.1   Upon receipt of a bank statement, which **one** of the following must be written into the firm's cash book?

(a)	Payment debited in error by the bank	
(b)	Unpresented cheques	
(c)	Electronic transfers from customers	
(d)	Outstanding lodgements	

3.2   A firm's bank statement shows an overdraft of £600. Unpresented cheques total £250; outstanding lodgements total £1,000. What is the balance at bank shown by the cash book?

(a)	£150 debit	
(b)	£650 debit	
(c)	£250 credit	
(d)	£150 credit	

3.3   Show whether the following statements are true or false.

Statement	True	False
(a) Some differences between the bank statement and the cash book are described as timing differences – these are not corrected in the cash book		
(b) A trade receivable's cheque is unpaid – the amount of the unpaid cheque must be recorded in cash book on the debit side		
(c) In a bank reconciliation statement which starts with the closing bank statement balance, unpresented cheques are deducted		
(d) The opening cash book balance at bank will always be the same as the opening bank statement balance		

3.4   Complete the following text by choosing the correct words from the boxes below and entering them in the boxes in the text.

cash book	bank statement	ledger	error
discrepancy	fraud	regular	daily
timing	date	independent	similarity

It is important to reconcile the cash book to the [   ]

on a [   ] basis.

The bank statement provides an [   ] accounting

record and helps to prevent [   ] .

It also highlights any [   ] differences and explains

why there is a [   ] between the closing bank statement

balance and the closing [   ] balance.

3.5   The bank statement and cash book of Garvey Ltd for the month of June are shown below.

BANK STATEMENT

Date 20-4	Details	Paid out £	Paid in £	Balance £
01 Jun	Balance b/f			2,685 C
02 Jun	Cheque 784342	855		1,830 C
07 Jun	BACS credit: P Parker		1,525	3,355 C
08 Jun	Cheque 784344	697		2,658 C
10 Jun	Cheque 784345	1,922		736 C
14 Jun	Counter credit		2,607	3,343 C
15 Jun	Cheque 784343	412		2,931 C
18 Jun	BACS credit: Watson Ltd		2,109	5,040 C
24 Jun	Direct debit: First Electric	112		4,928 C
24 Jun	Cheque 784347	1,181		3,747 C
25 Jun	Bank charges	45		3,702 C
28 Jun	Cheque 784348	594		3,108 C

D = Debit   C = Credit

CASH BOOK

Date 20-4	Details	Bank £	Date 20-4	Cheque number	Details	Bank £
1 Jun	Balance b/f	1,830	3 Jun	784343	Gladysz & Co	412
5 Jun	P Parker	1,525	3 Jun	784344	Daley Ltd	697
10 Jun	Dunlevy Ltd	2,607	3 Jun	784345	Ward & Lamb	1,922
25 Jun	Corline Traders	1,433	12 Jun	784346	Hendrie Stores	692
28 Jun	Moss & Co	786	12 Jun	784347	McCabes	1,181
			12 Jun	784348	Rehman Ltd	594
			24 Jun		First Electric	112
			29 Jun	784349	Hannaford & Co	764
			30 Jun		Balance c/d	1,807

You are to update the cash book and to prepare a bank reconciliation statement at 30 June 20-8.

Cash book	Debit £	Credit £
Closing balance b/d		
Adjustments:		
Adjusted balance c/d		

Bank reconciliation	£
Closing bank statement balance	3,108
Less unpresented cheques:	
Add outstanding lodgements:	
Adjusted closing cash book balance	

Select your entries from the following list: Bank charges, Corline Traders, Daley Ltd, Dunlevy Ltd, First Electric, Gladysz & Co, Hannaford & Co, Hendrie Stores, McCabes, Moss & Co, P Parker, Rehman Ltd, Ward & Lamb, Watson Ltd.

3.6 Complete the following text by choosing the correct words from the boxes below and entering them in the boxes in the text.

cash book	timing differences	bank	errors

security	reconciliation	authorised

The bank [   ] explains any difference between the closing

balance in the [   ] and the closing balance at the

[   ] .

It highlights any [   ] and [   ] .

Access to bank records should be restricted to [   ]

employees to safeguard the [   ] of payments and receipts.

3.7 Identify whether each of the following statements is true or false.

Statement	True	False
Unpresented cheques and outstanding lodgements are examples of timing differences		
Bank charges shown on the bank statement are recorded on the debit side of the cash book		
The opening cash book balance is always the same as the opening bank statement balance		

4 Use of control accounts

4.1 You have the following information for the month:

- customer balances at start of month — £25,685
- credit sales — £18,732
- sales returns — £876
- money received from customers — £17,455
- discounts allowed — £227
- irrecoverable debt written off — £175

What is the figure for customer balances at the end of the month?

(a)	£23,130	
(b)	£25,684	
(c)	£25,686	
(d)	£26,034	

4.2 You have the following information for the month:

- supplier balances at start of month — £13,278
- credit purchases — £9,584
- purchases returns — £821
- money paid to suppliers — £10,058
- discounts received — £247

What is the figure for supplier balances at the end of the month?

(a)	£12,230	
(b)	£13,378	
(c)	£11,736	
(d)	£14,820	

4.3 You have the following information for the month:

- balance of VAT account at start of month   £2,380   credit
- VAT from sales day book   £1,420
- VAT from purchases day book   £1,030
- VAT from discounts allowed day book   £35
- VAT from sales returns day book   £223
- VAT from purchases returns day book   £185
- VAT from discounts received day book   £22
- VAT from cash sales   £570

What is the balance of VAT account at the end of the month?

(a)	£1,471 debit
(b)	£1,471 credit
(c)	£3,289 debit
(d)	£3,289 credit

4.4 **(a)** The following is a summary of transactions with credit customers during the month of July.

Show by ticking the appropriate column whether each entry will be a debit or credit in the receivables ledger control account in the general ledger.

Receivables ledger control account

Details	Amount £	Debit	Credit
Balance owing from credit customers at 1 July	7,298		
Money received from credit customers	6,450		
Discounts allowed	75		
Goods sold to credit customers	14,774		
Goods returned by credit customers	501		
Journal credit to correct an error	89		

(b)   The following is a summary of transactions with credit suppliers during the month of July.

Show by ticking the appropriate column whether each entry will be a debit or credit in the payables ledger control account in the general ledger.

Payables ledger control account

Details	Amount £	Debit	Credit
Balance owing to credit suppliers at 1 July	2,299		
Money paid to credit suppliers	2,276		
Discounts received	23		
Goods purchased from credit suppliers	5,113		
Goods returned to credit suppliers	108		

At the beginning of September the following balances were in the receivables ledger:

Credit customers	Balances	
	Amount £	Debit/credit
J Stone	1,992	Debit
Murray Ltd	2,464	Debit
Parton & Co	320	Credit
Davies Ltd	411	Debit
Carpenter Ltd	2,569	Debit
King & Co	1,945	Debit

(c)   What should the balance of the receivables ledger control account be on 1 September in order for it to reconcile with the total of the balances in the receivables ledger?

Balance	
(a) Debit balance of £9,701	
(b) Credit balance of £9,701	
(c) Debit balance of £9,061	
(d) Credit balance of £9,061	

(d)   Show whether the following statements are true or false.

		True	False
(a)	If an irrecoverable debt is not written off in the receivables ledger control account, the balance on the account will be lower than it should be		
(b)	The balance of the payables ledger control account should agree with the total of the aged trade payables analysis		
(c)	Reconciliation of the receivables ledger control account highlights any differences between the subsidiary ledger total and the control account balance		

4.5 You work as an accounts assistant for Tilsley Trading. Today you are working on the payables ledger control account and payables ledger.

A summary of transactions with credit suppliers during the month of June is shown below.

(a) Show whether each entry will be a debit or a credit in the payables ledger control account in the general ledger.

Details	Amount £	Debit	Credit
Balance of credit suppliers at 1 June	35,106		
Purchases from credit suppliers	20,354		
Payments made to credit suppliers	19,062		
Discounts received	289		
Goods returned to credit suppliers	1,374		

(b) What will be the balance brought down on 1 July on the above account?

(a)	Dr £34,735	
(b)	Cr £34,735	
(c)	Dr £35,477	
(d)	Cr £35,477	
(e)	Dr £35,313	
(f)	Cr £35,313	

The following credit balances were in the payables ledger on 1 July.

	£
Cockerill Ltd	9,262
Darnbrook & Co	3,495
M Warren	5,724
De Graaf Ltd	6,098
Hannaford Trading	4,477
Quesne plc	5,386

(c) Reconcile the balances shown above with the payables ledger control account balance calculated in part (b).

	£
Balance on payables ledger control account at 1 July	
Total of the payables ledger balances at 1 July	
Difference	

(d) What may have caused the difference you calculated in part (c)?

(a)	An amount for discounts received was entered twice in the payables ledger control account	
(b)	A credit note was not entered in the payables ledger control account	
(c)	A credit note was not entered in the payables ledger	
(d)	An amount for discounts received was not entered in the payables ledger	

4.6   You work as an Accounts Assistant for Wyvern Windows. Today you are working on the receivables ledger control account and receivables ledger. A summary of transactions with credit customers during the month of April is shown below.

(a)   Show whether each entry will be a debit or a credit in the receivables ledger control account in the general ledger.

Details	Amount £	Debit	Credit
Balance of credit customers at 1 April	18,392		
Goods sold to credit customers	6,874		
Money received from credit customers	8,937		
Discounts allowed	154		
Goods returned by credit customers	529		

(b)   What will be the balance brought down on 1 May on the above account?

(a) Dr £17,012	
(b) Cr £17,012	
(c) Dr £15,646	
(d) Cr £15,646	
(e) Dr £21,138	
(f) Cr £21,138	

The following debit balances were in the receivables ledger on 1 May.

	£
Hamilton Ltd	3,486
Gusson & Co	1,089
Palgrave Supplies	2,627
Ikpusu & Co	4,321
Lorenz Ltd	747
McDiarmid plc	3,961

(c)   Reconcile the balances shown above with the receivables ledger control account balance calculated in part (b).

	£
Balance on receivables ledger control account at 1 May	
Total of the receivables ledger balances at 1 May	
Difference	

(d)   What may have caused the difference you calculated in part (c)?

(a)	An invoice was entered twice in the receivables ledger	
(b)	A credit note was entered twice in the receivables ledger	
(c)	A credit note was not entered in the receivables ledger control account	
(d)	An amount of discounts allowed was not entered in the receivables ledger control account	

(e)   Tick **two** of the following statements that are true.

(a)	Reconciliation of the payables ledger control account assures managers that the amount showing as outstanding to suppliers is correct	
(b)	The balance of the payables ledger control account should agree with the total of the balances in the receivables ledger	
(c)	The balance of the receivables ledger control account should agree with the total of the aged trade payables analysis	
(d)	Reconciliation of the receivables ledger control account highlights any differences between the subsidiary ledger total and the control account balance	

4.7   You work as an Accounts Assistant for Craven Cottages Ltd. Today you are working on the VAT control account.

The following figures have been taken from Craven Cottages' books of prime entry:

Totals for quarter

Sales day book	
Net	£68,800
VAT	£13,760
Total	£82,560

Purchases day book	
Net	£35,000
VAT	£7,000
Total	£42,000

Sales returns day book	
Net	£2,240
VAT	£448
Total	£2,688

Purchases returns day book	
Net	£1,640
VAT	£328
Total	£1,968

Cash book: cash-sales	
Net	£2,840
VAT	£568
Total	£3,408

Discounts allowed day book	
Net	£600
VAT	£120
Total	£720

(a)   What will be the entries in the VAT control account to record the VAT transactions in the quarter?

Select your entries for the details columns from the following list: Cash sales, Discounts allowed, Discounts allowed day book, Purchases, Purchases day book, Purchases returns, Purchases returns day book, Sales, Sales day book, Sales returns, Sales returns day book, Value Added Tax.

VAT control account

Details	Amount £	Details	Amount £

(b)   The VAT Return has been completed and shows an amount owing to HM Revenue & Customs of £6,432.

Is the VAT Return correct?

Yes	
No	

4.8   The following is a list of the VAT totals from the books of prime entry of a business:

Books of prime entry	VAT totals for quarter £
Sales day book	14,800
Purchases day book	9,080
Sales returns day book	368
Purchases returns day book	248
Cash book: cash sales	376

Other VAT items for the quarter are as follows:

VAT on petty cash payments	17
VAT on irrecoverable debts written off	108
VAT on purchase of computer equipment	575
VAT paid to HMRC	9,804

(a)   What will be the entries in the VAT control account to record the VAT transactions in the quarter?

Select your entries for the details column from the following list: Bank, Cash sales, Computer equipment, Irrecoverable debts, Petty cash, Purchases, Purchases day book, Purchases returns, Purchases returns day book, Sales, Sales day book, Sales returns, Sales returns day book, VAT.

VAT control account

Details	Amount £	Details	Amount £
		Balance b/f	9,804

(b)   The VAT Return has been completed and shows an amount owing to HM Revenue & Customs of £5,276.

Is the VAT Return correct?

Yes	
No	

(c)   Show whether the following statements are true or false.

	True	False
(a) The VAT control account is used to calculate how much VAT is due to, or sometimes from, HM Revenue & Customs		
(b) A debit balance on the VAT control account indicates that the business is due a refund from HM Revenue & Customs		
(c) A bank payment of VAT due to HM Revenue & Customs will be entered as a debit in the VAT control account		

4.9   The following is a record of the VAT values in the books of prime entry of a business:

	£
VAT from Sales day book	17,080
VAT from Sales returns day book	280
VAT from Purchases day book	9,800
VAT from Purchases returns day book	760
VAT from Discounts received day book	120
VAT from Cash book (VAT on cash sales)	192
VAT on petty cash payments	9
VAT on irrecoverable debt written off	82
VAT on purchase of studio equipment	400
VAT paid to HMRC	6,536

(a)   What will be the entries in the VAT control account to record the VAT transactions in the quarter?

Select your entries for the details columns from the following list: Bank, Cash book, Discounts received, Discounts received day book, Irrecoverable debts, Petty cash, Purchases, Purchases returns, Sales, Sales returns, Studio equipment, VAT.

VAT control account

Details	Amount £	Details	Amount £
		Balance b/f	6,536

The VAT Return has been completed and shows an amount owing to HM Revenue & Customs of £7,581.

(b)   Is the VAT Return correct?

Yes	
No	

(c)   Show whether the following statements are true or false.

	True	False
(a) VAT on purchases and expenses can only be entered in the VAT account if the purchase document bears the VAT registration number of the supplier		
(b) A bank receipt of a refund of VAT from HM Revenue & Customs would be entered as a credit in the VAT control account		
(c) A bank payment of VAT due to HM Revenue & Customs will be entered as a credit in the VAT control account		

4.10 **(a)** Identify which **one** of the following statements is correct in relation to the payables ledger control account.

Statement	
An entry made in the wrong payables ledger account will be revealed by the payables ledger control account	
The gross figure from purchases returns day book is debited to payables ledger control account	
Discounts received are not recorded in payables ledger control account	
A debit balance brought down on payables ledger control account indicates an error in the bookkeeping system	

You work in the accounts department of Morwenna Limited. Your manager asks you to prepare the receivables ledger control account for August.

The following transactions have been recorded with credit customers during the month of August:

Transaction	Amount £
Balance owing from credit customers at 1 August	10,686
Sales	7,104
Bank receipts	6,397
Sales returns	121
Discounts allowed	205
Irrecoverable debts written off	176

(b) Complete the receivables ledger control account below for August, including the balance carried down at the end of the month.

Receivables ledger control account			
Details	£	Details	£

5   The journal

5.1   Which **one** of the following transactions will be recorded in the journal?

(a)	Purchase of goods on credit	
(b)	Payroll transactions	
(c)	Goods returned by a credit customer	
(d)	Sale of goods for cash	

5.2   Mohammed Pazir started in business on 1 February 20-4 with the following assets and liabilities:

	£
Vehicle	6,500
Fixtures and fittings	2,800
Inventory	4,100
Cash	150
Bank	1,250
Loan from uncle	5,000

Use the form below to prepare Mohammed's opening journal entry, showing clearly his capital at 1 February 20-4.

Date 20-4	Details	Reference	Dr £	Cr £
	Journal entries to record the opening entries of the new business.			

5.3 You are employed by Sachdev Supplies as an Accounts Assistant. Today the Accounts Supervisor tells you that a credit customer, Lefroy Limited, has ceased trading, owing Sachdev Supplies £560 plus VAT at 20%.

(a) Record the journal entries needed in the general ledger to write off the net amount and the VAT.

Select your account names from the following list: Irrecoverable debts, Lefroy Limited, Payables ledger control, Purchases, Receivables ledger control, Sachdev Supplies, Sales, Value Added Tax.

Account name	Debit £	Credit £

(b) Sachdev Supplies has started a new business, Sachdev Developments, and a new set of accounts is to be opened. A partially completed journal to record the opening entries is shown below.

Record the journal entries needed in the accounts in the general ledger of Sachdev Developments to deal with the opening entries.

Account name	Amount £	Debit	Credit
Receivables ledger control	14,275		
Payables ledger control	7,392		
Inventory	4,107		
Office equipment	10,400		
Cash at bank	2,822		
Rent and rates	4,086		
Miscellaneous expenses	794		
Wages	2,397		
Loan from bank	6,250		
Capital	25,239		
Journal entries to record the opening entries of the new business			

5.4 You are employed by Mullen Limited as an Accounts Assistant.

Mullen Limited pays its employees through the bank every month and maintains a wages control account. A summary of last month's payroll transactions is shown below.

Item	£
Wages expense*	24,489
Income tax	2,510
Employer's National Insurance contributions	1,105
Employees' National Insurance contributions	965
Employer's pension contributions	1,032
Employees' pension contributions	1,032

*Tutorial note: Wages expense is the total cost of the payroll to the employer – that is, gross wages of employees (before deductions) + employer's NIC + employer's pension contributions.

Show the journal entries needed to record:

• the wages expense

• the HM Revenue & Customs liability

• the net wages paid to employees

• the pension fund liability

Select your account names from the following list: Bank, Employees' National Insurance, Employer's National Insurance, HM Revenue & Customs, Income tax, Net wages, Pension fund, Wages control, Wages expense.

Journal to record the wages expense

Account name	Debit £	Credit £

Journal to record the HM Revenue & Customs liability

Account name	Debit £	Credit £

Journal to record the net wages paid to employees

Account name	Debit £	Credit £

Journal to record the pension fund liability

Account name	Debit £	Credit £

5.5   Show which **four** of the following transactions would be entered in the journal.

(a)	Bank loan repayment	
(b)	Irrecoverable debt written off	
(c)	Opening entries at start of business	
(d)	Payment of VAT owing to HMRC	
(e)	Payroll transactions	
(f)	Purchase of non-current assets	
(g)	Transfer of cash from cash sales to bank	

5.6   Identify which **two** of the following situations are a correct use of the journal.

Situation	
Tamsin wishes to write off a receivables account from receivables ledger as an irrecoverable debt	
Hanna has bought postage stamps, paying for them from petty cash	
Imogen runs a furniture shop and she has sold furniture on credit to Wyvern Hotel Ltd	
Ernesto is setting up in business and is starting with capital of £10,000, office equipment valued at £2,500 and cash in the bank of £7,500	

5.7   A journal entry for payroll transactions is as follows:

31 March 20-6		Journal number: 81	
Account	**Debit** £	**Credit** £	**Description**
Wages expense	45,382		Gross pay
Bank		36,064	Net pay
Wages expense	5,106		Employer's NIC*
HMRC		5,106	Employer's NIC
HMRC		4,210	Employees' NIC
HMRC		5,108	Income tax (PAYE)

* National Insurance Contributions

Prior to this journal entry, the balance of the HM Revenue & Customs account was debit £1,270.

Show the transactions to be recorded on the HM Revenue & Customs account, calculate the balance carried down after these entries, and total both sides of the account (dates are not required).

HM Revenue & Customs			
Details	**£**	**Details**	**£**
Balance b/d	1,270		

6 The trial balance

6.1 Which **one** of the following accounts always has a credit balance?

(a)	Drawings account	
(b)	Sales returns account	
(c)	Sales account	
(d)	Office equipment account	

6.2 Which **one** of the following accounts always has a debit balance?

(a)	Purchases returns account	
(b)	Receivables ledger control account	
(c)	Capital account	
(d)	Loan account	

6.3   Prepare the initial trial balance of Kate Trelawney as at 31 March 20-2. She has omitted to open a capital account. **You are to** fill in the missing figure in order to balance the trial balance.

	£
Bank loan	3,650
Purchases	23,745
Vehicle	9,500
Sales	65,034
Bank (cash at bank)	2,162
Discounts allowed	317
Purchases returns	855
Receivables ledger control	7,045
Office equipment	5,450
Inventory at 1 April 20-1	4,381
Sales returns	1,624
Payables ledger control	4,736
Expenses	32,598
Discounts received	494
Capital	?

6.4   You work as an accounts assistant for Wyvern Trading. The accounts supervisor has asked you to work on preparing an initial trial balance as at 31 December 20-8. The supervisor has given you the following list of balances to be transferred to the trial balance.

You are to place the figures in the debit or credit column, as appropriate, and to total each column.

Account name	Amount £	Debit £	Credit £
Bank (overdraft)	4,293		
Loan from bank	12,500		
Vehicles	25,500		
Inventory	10,417		
Petty cash	68		
Capital	25,794		
VAT owing to HM Revenue & Customs	1,496		
Payables ledger control	12,794		
Purchases	104,763		
Purchases returns	2,681		
Receivables ledger control	28,354		
Sales	184,267		
Sales returns	4,098		
Discounts allowed	1,312		
Discounts received	1,784		
Wages	35,961		
Telephone	3,474		
Advertising	5,921		
Insurance	3,084		
Heating and lighting	2,477		
Rent and rates	3,672		
Postages	876		
Miscellaneous expenses	545		
Drawings	15,087		
Totals	–		

6.5   You work as an accounts assistant for Highley Limited. The accounts supervisor has asked you to work on preparing an initial trial balance as at 30 June 20-1. The supervisor has given you the following list of balances to be transferred to the trial balance.

You are to place the figures in the debit or credit column, as appropriate, and to total each column.

Account name	Amount £	Debit £	Credit £
Sales	262,394		
Sales returns	2,107		
Receivables ledger control	33,844		
Purchases	157,988		
Purchases returns	1,745		
Payables ledger control	17,311		
Discount received	1,297		
Discount allowed	845		
Rent and rates	5,941		
Advertising	6,088		
Insurance	3,176		
Wages	48,954		
Heating and lighting	4,266		
Postages and telephone	2,107		
Miscellaneous expenses	632		
Vehicles	28,400		
Capital	48,756		
Drawings	19,354		
Office equipment	10,500		
Inventory	16,246		
Petty cash	150		
Bank (cash at bank)	3,096		
VAT owing to HM Revenue & Customs	3,721		
Loan from bank	8,470		
Totals	–		

6.6 You are an accounts assistant at Dowson Trade Supplies.

Most of the ledger accounts have been closed off and the balances included in the trial balance at 31 July 20-6.

(a) You are to complete the remaining ledger accounts by inserting the balance carried down on each account. Enter your answers to two decimal places.

Bank					
20-6	**Details**	**£**	**20-6**	**Details**	**£**
1 Jul	Balance b/d	2,836.18	20 Jul	Stationery	746.29
6 Jul	Sales	5,107.29	25 Jul	Purchases	3,846.32
31 Jul	Receivables ledger control	25,391.18	31 Jul	Payables ledger control	21,234.96
			31 Jul	Balance c/d	

Discounts allowed					
20-6	**Details**	**£**	**20-6**	**Details**	**£**
1 Jul	Balance b/d	346.29			
31 Jul	Receivables ledger control	108.33			
			31 July	Balance c/d	

Payables ledger control					
20-6	**Details**	**£**	**20-6**	**Details**	**£**
31 Jul	Bank	21,234.96	1 Jul	Balance b/d	30,384.32
			14 Jul	Purchases	6,107.85
31 Jul	Balance c/d		28 Jul	Purchases	3,209.96

VAT control					
20-6	**Details**	**£**	**20-6**	**Details**	**£**
31 Jul	Purchases	2,318.40	1 Jul	Balance b/d	1,608.96
			31 Jul	Sales	3,220.14
31 Jul	Balance c/d				

(b) Complete the trial balance by inserting the missing figures and calculating the totals for each column. Enter your answers to two decimal places.

Item	Debit £	Credit £
Sales		122,831.15
Purchases	68,022.56	
Bank		
Discounts allowed		
Wages and salaries	33,290.42	
Office expenses	12,387.16	
Payables ledger control		
Receivables ledger control	22,147.18	
VAT control		
Totals		

7 Correction of errors

7.1 Fill in the missing words from the following sentences, choosing from:

omission   commission   principle   original entry   reversal of entries   compensating

(a) "You made an error of [ ] when you debited the cost of diesel fuel for the van to Vans Account."

(b) "I've had an email from the accounts supervisor at Jones Limited concerning the statements of account that we sent out the other day. She says that there is a sales invoice charged that she knows nothing about. I wonder if it should be for T Jones' account and we have made an error of [ ]?"

(c) "There is a 'bad figure' on a purchases invoice – we have read it as £35 when it should be £55. It has gone through our accounts wrongly so we have an error of [ ] to put right."

(d) "Although the trial balance balanced last week, I've since found an error of £100 in the calculation of the balance of sales account. We will need to check the other balances as I think we may have a [ ] error."

(e) "Who was in charge of that trainee last week? He has entered the payment for the electricity bill on the debit side of the bank and on the credit side of electricity – a [ ]."

(f) "I found this purchase invoice from last week in amongst the copy statements. As we haven't put it through the accounts we have an error of [ ]."

7.2 Telephone expenses of £250 paid from the bank have been debited to the bank columns of the cash book and credited to the telephone expenses account. Which one of the following entries will correct the error?

Debit			Credit		
(a)	Bank	£250	Telephone expenses	£250	
(b)	Telephone expenses	£250	Bank	£250	
(c)	Bank	£500	Telephone expenses	£500	
(d)	Telephone expenses	£500	Bank	£500	

7.3 The trial balance of Tairo Traders does not balance. The debit column totals £220,472 and the credit column totals £217,647.

(a) What entry will be made in the suspense account to balance the trial balance?

Account name	Debit £	Credit £
Suspense		

(b) It is important to understand the effects of errors in a bookkeeping system.

Show which of the errors below will cause an imbalance in the trial balance by placing a tick in the appropriate column for each error.

Error		Will cause an imbalance in the trial balance	Will not cause an imbalance in the trial balance
(a)	The cost of diesel fuel, £50, has been debited in the cash book and credited to vehicles account		
(b)	A credit sale of £225 has not been entered in the accounts		
(c)	The balance of wages account has been calculated incorrectly		
(d)	A cash purchase of £85 has been recorded in the cash book only		
(e)	The cost of stationery, £54, has been recorded as £45 in the cash book and stationery account		
(f)	Rent paid of £450 has been debited to rent paid account and debited in the cash book		

7.4   The initial trial balance of Merrett Marketing at 30 June 20-3 did not balance. The difference of £424 was placed into a suspense account.

The error has been traced to the purchases day book as shown below.

Purchases day book

Date 20-3	Details	Invoice number	Total £	VAT £	Net £
30 Jun	Downing Traders	2798	720	120	600
30 Jun	Morwenna and Co	M/2348	576	96	480
30 Jun	Oades plc	4592	1,248	208	1,040
	Totals		2,120	424	2,120

(a)   Identify the error and record the journal entries needed in the general ledger to:

- remove the incorrect entry

- record the correct entry

- remove the suspense account balance

Select your account name from the following list: Downing Traders, Morwenna and Co, Oades plc, Purchases, Purchases day book, Payables ledger control, Purchases returns, Purchases returns day book, Sales, Sales day book, Receivables ledger control, Sales returns, Sales returns day book, Suspense, Value Added Tax.

Journal to remove the incorrect entry

Account name	Debit £	Credit £

Journal to record the correct entry

Account name	Debit £	Credit £

Journal to remove the suspense account balance

Account name	Debit £	Credit £

An entry to record a bank payment of £525 for rent paid has been reversed.

(b)   Record the journal entries needed in the general ledger to:

  •   remove the incorrect entry

  •   record the correct entry

Select your account names from the following list: Bank, Cash, Purchases, Payables ledger control, Rent, Sales, Receivables ledger control, Suspense, Value Added Tax.

Journal to remove the incorrect entry

Account name	Debit £	Credit £

Journal to record the correct entry

Account name	Debit £	Credit £

7.5   A direct debit for business rates of £609 has been entered in the accounts as £690.

(a)   Record the journal entries needed in the general ledger to remove the incorrect entry.

Select your account names from the following list: Bank, Cash, Direct debit, Purchases, Rates, Suspense.

Account name	Debit £	Credit £

(b)   Record the journal entries needed in the general ledger to record the correct entry.

Select your account names from the following list: Bank, Cash, Direct debit, Purchases, Rates, Suspense.

Account name	Debit £	Credit £

7.6 The trial balance of Fayer and Co included a suspense account. All the bookkeeping errors have now been traced and the journal entries shown below have been recorded.

Journal entries

Account name	Debit £	Credit £
Office expenses	180	
Office equipment		180
Sales returns	295	
Suspense		295
Vehicle expenses	350	
Suspense		350

As the accounts assistant at Fayer and Co, **you are to** show the journal entries in the general ledger accounts. Dates are not required.

Select your entries for the details column from the following list: Balance b/f, Office equipment, Office expenses, Sales returns, Suspense, Vehicle expenses.

Office expenses

Details	Amount £	Details	Amount £

Office equipment

Details	Amount £	Details	Amount £

Sales returns

Details	Amount £	Details	Amount £

Suspense

Details	Amount £	Details	Amount £
Balance b/f	645		

Vehicle expenses

Details	Amount £	Details	Amount £

7.7   The trial balance of Quaver Music included a suspense account. All the bookkeeping errors have now been traced and the journal entries are shown below.

Account name	Debit	Credit
Sales	99	
Suspense		99
Suspense	1,612	
VAT		1,612
Bank interest paid	52	
Bank charges		52

Show the journal entries in the general ledger accounts on the next page. Dates are not required.

Select your entries for the details column from: Bank charges, Bank interest paid, Sales, Suspense.

Sales

Details	Amount £	Details	Amount £

VAT

Details	Amount £	Details	Amount £

Bank interest paid

Details	Amount £	Details	Amount £

Bank charges

Details	Amount £	Details	Amount £

Suspense

Details	Amount £	Details	Amount £
		Balance b/f	1,513

7.8 On 30 June 20-9, Khela Krafts prepared an initial trial balance which did not balance, and a suspense account was opened. On 1 July, journal entries were prepared to correct the errors that had been found, and to clear the suspense account. The list of balances in the initial trial balance, and the journal entries to correct the errors, are shown below and on the next page.

As the accounts assistant at Khela Krafts, **you are to** redraft the trial balance by placing the figures in the debit or credit column. You should take into account the journal entries (on the next page) which will clear the suspense account.

Account name	Balances on 30 June 20-9 £	Balances at 1 July 20-9 Debit £	Credit £
Inventory	8,692		
Receivables ledger control	12,347		
Petty cash	84		
Capital	15,287		
Loan from bank	8,625		
VAT owing to HM Revenue & Customs	2,733		
Payables ledger control	8,421		
Bank (cash at bank)	1,596		
Sales	77,364		
Sales returns	2,913		
Purchases	40,467		
Purchases returns	872		
Wages	20,644		
Advertising	2,397		
Insurance	1,849		
Heating and lighting	1,066		
Rent and business rates	3,862		
Vehicle expenses	2,035		
Vehicles	15,400		
Suspense account (credit balance)	50		
Totals			

Journal entries

Account name	Debit £	Credit £
Suspense	490	
Purchases returns		490

Account name	Debit £	Credit £
Suspense	320	
Vehicle expenses		320
Vehicle expenses	230	
Suspense		230

Account name	Debit £	Credit £
Advertising	530	
Suspense		530

7.9 The trial balance of Lizzie's business has disclosed that there are errors.

(a) Identify which **two** of the following statements about suspense accounts are true.

Statement	
A suspense account is created when errors are disclosed by the trial balance.	
A suspense account can have either a debit balance or a credit balance.	
When the debit side total of a trial balance is more than the credit side total, a suspense is opened with a debit balance.	
If the balance of receivables ledger control account does not agree with the total balances from receivables ledger, the difference should be transferred to suspense account.	

(b)   Identify whether each of the errors described below would or would not be disclosed by the trial balance.

Error	Disclosed	Not disclosed
A cash purchase has not been recorded in the accounts		
Payment for office expenses of £65 has been recorded in both office expenses account and bank account as £56		

7.10   Carissa and Hannah run a retail business. They use a manual accounting system and have prepared a trial balance at the year-end. The trial balance shows total debits of £54,684 and total credits of £53,897.

(a)   What is the balance of suspense account in the trial balance?

£ [   ]

This balance is (tick the answer):

Debit	
Credit	

Carissa and Hannah have identified the following errors:

Error 1: Rent received for April 20-6 of £850 was debited to bank account but was not recorded in rent received account.

Error 2: The day book total of purchases for May 20-6 was £13,118. The amount entered in purchases account in the general ledger was £13,181.

(b)   Complete the table below with the account names required to show the debits and credits that will be processed through the journal to clear suspense account.

31 May 20-6	Journal number 49		
Account	**Debit** £	**Credit** £	**Description**
	850		Correction of error 1
		850	Correction of error 1
	63		Correction of error 2
		63	Correction of error 2

7.11 You are an accounts assistant at Linton Trading. You are asked to redraft a trial balance after some errors have been identified and the correcting journal entries have been made.

The initial list of balances for Linton Trading at 30 April 20-4 is:

Item	£
Sales	78,242.99
Purchases	40,216.45
Discounts received	1,027.16
Bank	3,108.90
Office equipment	10,362.50
Receivables ledger control	24,595.13
Suspense	987.17

The errors have been identified and the following journal entries need to be processed:

Date: 30 April 20-4		Journal number: 087		
Date	Description	Debit £	Credit £	
30 April	Suspense	54.13		Discounts received not recorded in discounts received account
30 April	Discounts received		54.13	Discounts received not recorded in discounts received account
30 April	Purchases	1,041.30		Purchases of £520.65 recorded on credit side of purchases account
30 April	Suspense		1,041.30	Purchases of £520.65 recorded on credit side of purchases account

You are to complete the adjusted trial balance by inserting the correct figures in either the debit or credit column, and calculating the totals for each column.

Item	Debit £	Credit £
Sales		
Purchases		
Discounts received		
Bank		
Office equipment		
Receivables ledger control		
Totals		

Answers to chapter activities

1 Payment methods

1.1 (a) Employee wages

(c) The petty cash system

1.2 (b) Cheque

1.3

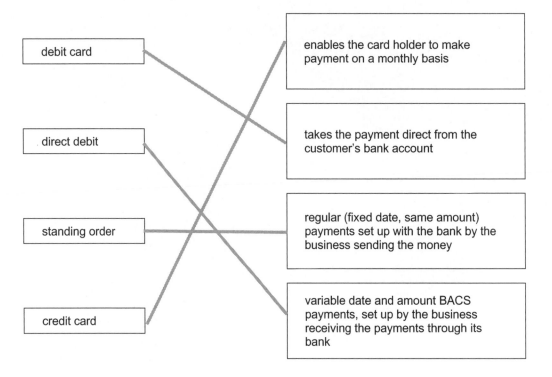

debit card	enables the card holder to make payment on a monthly basis
direct debit	takes the payment direct from the customer's bank account
standing order	regular (fixed date, same amount) payments set up with the bank by the business sending the money
credit card	variable date and amount BACS payments, set up by the business receiving the payments through its bank

1.4 **(a)**, **(c)** and **(d)** are false; **(b)** is true

1.5 A **standing order** is set up by the **payer's bank** and used to make fixed date payments for the same amount through the banking system.

A **direct debit** enables **variable amounts** to be taken from the payer's account and the payments are deducted through the **receiver's bank**.

1.6

		Option number
(a)	Paying rent for the office at a fixed amount of £750 a month	5
(b)	Paying insurance premium of £2,000 which increases every year	3
(c)	Buying office furniture for £1,200 from a local superstore	2
(d)	Paying solicitors fees of £500 plus VAT in connection with lease	4
(e)	Buying a travel card for £30 at the local railway station	1

1.7 **(a)** Error 1: The year is missing from the date

Error 2: The amount in words and figures is different

Error 3: The cheque has not been signed by the issuer

(b) (b) Contact T Witt Trading Ltd and ask for a new cheque to be issued

1.8

Description	Payment method
An instruction in writing signed by the bank's customer telling the bank to pay a one-off amount to a named person	Cheque
A card issued on a 'buy now and pay later' basis; payment is made monthly in full or in part	Credit card
A variable date and amount payment, set up by the business receiving the payments	Direct debit
A paper-based document issued by a bank and used for high value payments	Bank draft

2 Payment methods and the bank account balance

2.1 (a) The solvency of the business

(d) Keeping bank charges to a minimum

(e) Keeping interest on overdrafts to a minimum

2.2 (a) Keeping the bank account in credit whenever possible

(c) Encouraging customers to pay by Faster Payment

(e) Paying the business insurance costs by monthly standing order rather than in one payment at the beginning of the period of insurance

2.3 (a) Debit

(b) Credit

(c) Credit

(d) Debit

2.4 (a) Faster Payment

(c) CHAPS

(d) Bank draft

2.5 (a) Cheque paid in at a different bank

(d) Credit card

2.6

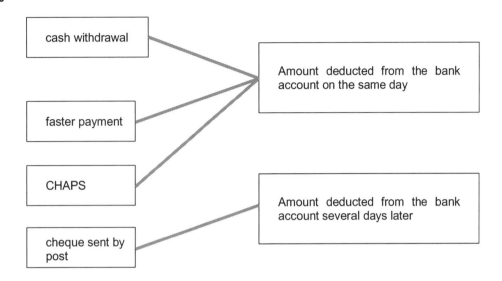

2.7 (b) Pay the invoice so that it reaches the supplier's bank as late as possible within the 30 day period

2.8 (a)

Statement	
It is good practice to pay cheques received during the month into the bank account at the end of the month	
A bank overdraft should be arranged in advance of being required	✔
A bank does not make a charge when it has to return unpaid cheques that its customer has issued	

(b)

Statement	True	False
A cheque paid in at a different bank or branch from the cheque issuer will be deducted from the issuer's account one working day later	✔	
A payment made by debit card is normally deducted from the bank account on the same working day		✔
A CHAPS electronic bank transfer is deducted from the sender's bank account on the day that the transfer is made	✔	

<table>
<tr><td>**3**</td><td>Bank reconciliation statements</td></tr>
</table>

3.1 (c) Electronic transfers from customers

3.2 (a) £150 debit

3.3 (a) and (c) true; (b) and (d) false

3.4 It is important to reconcile the cash book to the **bank statement** on a **regular** basis.

The bank statement provides an **independent** accounting record and helps to prevent **fraud**.

It also highlights any **timing** differences and explains why there is a **discrepancy** between the closing bank statement balance and the closing **cash book** balance.

3.5

Cash book	Debit £	Credit £
Closing balance b/d	1,807	
Adjustments:		
Watson Ltd	2,109	
Bank charges		45
Adjusted balance c/d		3,871

Bank reconciliation	£
Closing bank statement balance	3,108
Less unpresented cheques:	
Hendrie Stores	692
Hannaford & Co	764
Add outstanding lodgements:	
Corline Traders	1,433
Moss & Co	786
Adjusted closing cash book balance	3,871

3.6   The bank **reconciliation** explains any difference between the closing balance in the **cash book** and the closing balance at the **bank**.

It highlights any **errors** and **timing differences**.

Access to bank records should be restricted to **authorised** employees to safeguard the **security** of payments and receipts.

3.7   Identify whether each of the following statements is true or false.

Statement	True	False
Unpresented cheques and outstanding lodgements are examples of timing differences	✔	
Bank charges shown on the bank statement are recorded on the debit side of the cash book		✔
The opening cash book balance is always the same as the opening bank statement balance		✔

4 Use of control accounts

4.1 (b) £25,684

4.2 (c) £11,736

4.3 (d) £3,289 credit

4.4 (a) **Receivables ledger control account**

Details	Amount £	Debit	Credit
Balance owing from credit customers at 1 July	7,298	✔	
Money received from credit customers	6,450		✔
Discounts allowed	75		✔
Goods sold to credit customers	14,774	✔	
Goods returned by credit customers	501		✔
Journal credit to correct an error	89		✔

(b) **Payables ledger control account**

Details	Amount £	Debit	Credit
Balance owing to credit suppliers at 1 July	2,299		✔
Money paid to credit suppliers	2,276	✔	
Discounts received	23	✔	
Goods purchased from credit suppliers	5,113		✔
Goods returned to credit suppliers	108	✔	

(c) (c) Debit balance of £9,061

(d) (a) is false; (b) and (c) are true.

4.5   **(a)**

Details	Amount £	Debit	Credit
Balance of credit suppliers at 1 June	35,106		✔
Purchases from credit suppliers	20,354		✔
Payments made to credit suppliers	19,062	✔	
Discounts received	289	✔	
Goods returned to credit suppliers	1,374	✔	

(b)   (b)   Cr £34,735

(c)

	£
Balance on payables ledger control account at 1 July	34,735
Total of the payables ledger balances at 1 July	34,442
Difference	293

(d)   (b)   A credit note was not entered in the payables ledger control account

4.6   **(a)**

Details	Amount £	Debit	Credit
Balance of credit customers at 1 April	18,392	✔	
Goods sold to credit customers	6,874	✔	
Money received from credit customers	8,937		✔
Discounts allowed	154		✔
Goods returned by credit customers	529		✔

(b)   (c)   Dr £15,646

(c)

	£
Balance on receivables ledger control account at 1 May	15,646
Total of the receivables ledger balances at 1 May	16,231
Difference	585

(d)   (a)   An invoice was entered twice in the receivables ledger

(e)   (a) and (d) are true

4.7 **(a)**

VAT control account

Details	Amount £	Details	Amount £
Purchases	7,000	Sales	13,760
Sales returns	448	Purchases returns	328
Discounts allowed	120	Cash sales	568

(b) No

4.8 **(a)**

VAT control account

Details	Amount £	Details	Amount £
Purchases	9,080	Balance b/f	9,804
Sales returns	368	Sales	14,800
Petty cash	17	Purchases returns	248
Irrecoverable debts	108	Cash sales	376
Computer equipment	575		
Bank	9,804		

(b) Yes

(c) All statements are true.

4.9   **(a)**

VAT control account

Details	Amount £	Details	Amount £
Sales returns	280	Balance b/f	6,536
Purchases	9,800	Sales	17,080
Petty cash	9	Purchases returns	760
Irrecoverable debts	82	Discounts received	120
Studio equipment	400	Sales	192
Bank	6,536		

(b)   Yes

(c)   (a) and (b) are true; (c) is false.

4.10   **(a)**

Statement	
An entry made in the wrong payables ledger account will be revealed by the payables ledger control account	
The gross figure from purchases returns day book is debited to payables ledger control account	✔
Discounts received are not recorded in payables ledger control account	
A debit balance brought down on payables ledger control account indicates an error in the bookkeeping system	

(b)

Receivables ledger control account			
Details	£	Details	£
Balance b/d	10,686	Bank	6,397
Sales	7,104	Sales returns	121
		Discounts allowed	205
		Irrecoverable debts	176
		Balance c/d	10,891

5 The journal

5.1 (b) Payroll transactions

5.2

Date 20-4	Details	Reference	Dr £	Cr £
1 Feb	Vehicle	GL	6,500	
	Fixtures and fittings	GL	2,800	
	Inventory	GL	4,100	
	Cash	CB	150	
	Bank	CB	1,250	
	Loan from uncle	GL		5,000
	Capital	GL		9,800
			14,800	14,800
	Journal entries to record the opening entries of the new business.			

5.3 (a)

Account name	Debit £	Credit £
Irrecoverable debts	560	
Value Added Tax	112	
Receivables ledger control		672

(b)

Account name	Amount £	Debit	Credit
Receivables ledger control	14,275	✔	
Payables ledger control	7,392		✔
Inventory	4,107	✔	
Office equipment	10,400	✔	
Cash at bank	2,822	✔	
Rent and rates	4,086	✔	
Miscellaneous expenses	794	✔	
Wages	2,397	✔	
Loan from bank	6,250		✔
Capital	25,239		✔
Journal entries to record the opening entries of the new business			

5.4   **Journal to record the wages expense**

Account name	Debit £	Credit £
Wages expense	24,489	
Wages control		24,489

Journal to record the HM Revenue & Customs liability

Account name	Debit £	Credit £
Wages control	4,580	
HM Revenue & Customs		4,580

Journal to record the net wages paid to employees

Account name	Debit £	Credit £
Wages control	17,845	
Bank		17,845

Tutorial note: £24,489 – £2,510 – £1,105 – £965 – £1,032 – £1,032 = £17,845

Journal to record the pension fund liability

Account name	Debit £	Credit £
Wages control	2,064	
Pension fund		2,064

5.5 (b), (c), (e) and (f)

5.6

Situation	
Tamsin wishes to write off a receivables account from receivables ledger as an irrecoverable debt	✔
Hanna has bought postage stamps, paying for them from petty cash	
Imogen runs a furniture shop and she has sold furniture on credit to Wyvern Hotel Ltd	
Ernesto is setting up in business and is starting with capital of £10,000, office equipment valued at £2,500 and cash in the bank of £7,500	✔

5.7

HM Revenue & Customs			
Details	£	Details	£
Balance b/d	1,270	Employer's NIC	5,106
		Employees' NIC	4,210
Balance c/d	13,154	Income tax (PAYE)	5,108
	14,424		14,424

6 | The trial balance

6.1 (c) Sales account

6.2 (b) Receivables ledger control account

6.3 **Trial balance of Kate Trelawney as at 31 March 20-2**

Name of account	Dr £	Cr £
Bank loan		3,650
Purchases	23,745	
Vehicle	9,500	
Sales		65,034
Bank (cash at bank)	2,162	
Discounts allowed	317	
Purchases returns		855
Receivables ledger control	7,045	
Office equipment	5,450	
Inventory at 1 April 20-1	4,381	
Sales returns	1,624	
Payables ledger control		4,736
Expenses	32,598	
Discounts received		494
Capital *(missing figure)*		12,053
	86,822	86,822

6.4

Account name	Amount £	Debit £	Credit £
Bank (overdraft)	4,293		4,293
Loan from bank	12,500		12,500
Vehicles	25,500	25,500	
Inventory	10,417	10,417	
Petty cash	68	68	
Capital	25,794		25,794
VAT owing to HM Revenue & Customs	1,496		1,496
Payables ledger control	12,794		12,794
Purchases	104,763	104,763	
Purchases returns	2,681		2,681
Receivables ledger control	28,354	28,354	
Sales	184,267		184,267
Sales returns	4,098	4,098	
Discount allowed	1,312	1,312	
Discount received	1,784		1,784
Wages	35,961	35,961	
Telephone	3,474	3,474	
Advertising	5,921	5,921	
Insurance	3,084	3,084	
Heating and lighting	2,477	2,477	
Rent and rates	3,672	3,672	
Postages	876	876	
Miscellaneous expenses	545	545	
Drawings	15,087	15,087	
Totals	–	245,609	245,609

6.5

Account name	Amount £	Debit £	Credit £
Sales	262,394		262,394
Sales returns	2,107	2,107	
Receivables ledger control	33,844	33,844	
Purchases	157,988	157,988	
Purchases returns	1,745		1,745
Payables ledger control	17,311		17,311
Discount received	1,297		1,297
Discount allowed	845	845	
Rent and rates	5,941	5,941	
Advertising	6,088	6,088	
Insurance	3,176	3,176	
Wages	48,954	48,954	
Heating and lighting	4,266	4,266	
Postages and telephone	2,107	2,107	
Miscellaneous expenses	632	632	
Vehicles	28,400	28,400	
Capital	48,756		48,756
Drawings	19,354	19,354	
Office equipment	10,500	10,500	
Inventory	16,246	16,246	
Petty cash	150	150	
Bank (cash at bank)	3,096	3,096	
VAT owing to HM Revenue & Customs	3,721		3,721
Loan from bank	8,470		8,470
Totals	–	343,694	343,694

6.6   **(a)**   Bank: £7,507.08
Discounts allowed: £454.62
Payables ledger control: £18,467.17
VAT control: £2,510.70

(b)

Item	Debit £	Credit £
Sales		122,831.15
Purchases	68,022.56	
Bank	7,507.08	
Discounts allowed	454.62	
Wages and salaries	33,290.42	
Office expenses	12,387.16	
Payables ledger control		18,467.17
Receivables ledger control	22,147.18	
VAT control		2,510.70
Totals	143,809.02	143,809.02

7 Correction of errors

7.1 **(a)** Principle

(b) Commission

(c) Original entry

(d) Compensating

(e) Reversal of entries

(f) Omission

7.2

Debit		Credit	
(d)	Telephone expenses £500	Bank	£500

7.3 **(a)**

Account name	Debit £	Credit £
Suspense		2,825

(b) (c), (d) and (f) will cause an imbalance; (a), (b) and (e) will not.

7.4 **(a)** **Journal to remove the incorrect entry**

Account name	Debit £	Credit £
Payables ledger control	2,120	

Journal to record the correct entry

Account name	Debit £	Credit £
Payables ledger control		2,544

Journal to remove the suspense account balance

Account name	Debit £	Credit £
Suspense	424	

(b) **Journal to remove the incorrect entry**

Account name	Debit £	Credit £
Rent	525	
Bank		525

Journal to record the correct entry

Account name	Debit £	Credit £
Rent	525	
Bank		525

7.5   **(a)**

Account name	Debit £	Credit £
Bank	690	
Rates		690

(b)

Account name	Debit £	Credit £
Rates	609	
Bank		609

7.6

Office expenses

Details	Amount £	Details	Amount £
Office equipment	180		

Office equipment

Details	Amount £	Details	Amount £
		Office expenses	180

Sales returns

Details	Amount £	Details	Amount £
Suspense	295		

Suspense

Details	Amount £	Details	Amount £
Balance b/f	645	Sales returns	295
		Vehicle expenses	350

Vehicle expenses

Details	Amount £	Details	Amount £
Suspense	350		

7.7

Sales

Details	Amount £	Details	Amount £
Suspense	99		

VAT

Details	Amount £	Details	Amount £
		Suspense	1,612

Bank interest paid

Details	Amount £	Details	Amount £
Bank charges	52		

Bank charges

Details	Amount £	Details	Amount £
		Bank interest paid	52

Suspense

Details	Amount £	Details	Amount £
VAT	1,612	Balance b/f	1,513
		Sales	99

7.8

Account name	Balances on 30 June 20-9	Balances at 1 July 20-9	
	£	Debit £	Credit £
Inventory	8,692	8,692	
Receivables ledger control	12,347	12,347	
Petty cash	84	84	
Capital	15,287		15,287
Loan from bank	8,625		8,625
VAT owing to HM Revenue & Customs	2,733		2,733
Payables ledger control	8,421		8,421
Bank (cash at bank)	1,596	1,596	
Sales	77,364		77,364
Sales returns	2,913	2,913	
Purchases	40,467	40,467	
Purchases returns	872		1,362
Wages	20,644	20,644	
Advertising	2,397	2,927	
Insurance	1,849	1,849	
Heating and lighting	1,066	1,066	
Rent and business rates	3,862	3,862	
Vehicle expenses	2,035	1,945	
Vehicles	15,400	15,400	
Suspense account (credit balance)	50	–	–
Totals		113,792	113,792

7.9 **(a)**

Statement	
A suspense account is created when errors are disclosed by the trial balance	✔
A suspense account can have either a debit balance or a credit balance	✔
When the debit side total of a trial balance is more than the credit side total, a suspense is opened with a debit balance	
If the balance of receivables ledger control account does not agree with the total balances from receivables ledger, the difference should be transferred to suspense account	

(b)

Error	Disclosed	Not disclosed
A cash purchase has not been recorded in the accounts		✔
Payment for office expenses of £65 has been recorded in both office expenses account and bank account as £56		✔

7.10 **(a)**   £787 Credit

(b)

31 May 20-6			Journal number 49
Account	**Debit** £	**Credit** £	**Description**
Suspense	850		Correction of error 1
Rent received		850	Correction of error 1
Suspense	63		Correction of error 2
Purchases		63	Correction of error 2

Tutorial note: the difference of £63 has been entered here. An alternative treatment is to take out the wrong figure of £13,181 (debit suspense; credit purchases) and then record the correct figure of £13,118 (debit purchases; credit suspense). The effect is the same as the net amount of £63 shown above.

7.11

Item	Debit £	Credit £
Sales		78,242.99
Purchases	41,257.75	
Discounts received		1,081.29
Bank	3,108.90	
Office equipment	10,362.50	
Receivables ledger control	24,595.13	
Totals	79,324.28	79,324.28

Practice assessment 1

Assessment information

- This practice assessment contains **8 tasks** and you should attempt to complete **every** task.

- Each task is independent. You will not need to refer to your answers from previous tasks.

- Read every task carefully to make sure you understand what is required.

- Where the date is relevant, it is given in the task data.

- Both minus signs and brackets can be used to indicate negative numbers **unless** task instructions state otherwise.

- You must use a full stop to indicate a decimal point. For example, write 100.57 **not** 100,57 or 10057.

- You may use a comma to indicate a number in the thousands, but you don't have to. For example, 10000 and 10,000 are both acceptable.

- Mathematical rounding should be applied where appropriate.

Task 1

This task is about using control accounts.

A receivables ledger control account balance is shown in general ledger.

(a) Identify which **one** of the following statements is correct in relation to the receivables ledger control account.

Statement	
An entry made in the wrong receivables ledger account will be revealed by the receivables ledger control account	
The net figure from sales day book is debited to receivables ledger control account	
Irrecoverable debts written off are not recorded in receivables ledger control account	
The balance of receivables ledger control account gives a total figure for the amount owing by credit customers	

You work in the accounts department of Hamid Limited. Your manager asks you to prepare the VAT control account for July.

The following transactions have been recorded during the month of July:

Transaction	Amount £
VAT owing to HM Revenue & Customs at 1 July	1,585
VAT on sales	2,627
VAT on purchases	1,345
VAT on sales returns	205
VAT on purchases returns	286
VAT on discounts received	154
VAT on discounts allowed	122
VAT on cash sales	728
VAT payment made to HM Revenue & Customs	1,585

(b) Complete the VAT control account below for July, including the balance carried down at the end of the month.

VAT control account			
Details	**£**	**Details**	**£**
		Balance b/d	
Balance c/d			

JP Limited has the following payables ledger control account.

Payables ledger control account					
Date **20-2**	**Details**	**£**	**Date** **20-2**	**Details**	**£**
31 May	Bank	28,460	1 May	Balance b/d	6,240
31 May	Purchases returns	1,045	31 May	Purchases	32,680
31 May	Discounts received	210			
31 May	Balance c/d				

(c) What is the balance carried down on the payables ledger control account at 31 May 20-2?

£ [   ]

Task 2

This task is about reconciling control accounts.

The balance of the payables ledger control account will be used in the year-end trial balance. It is important to reconcile this to the payables ledger.

(a)   Identify which **one** of the following statements is a reason for completing this reconciliation.

Statement	
Entries made in the wrong payables ledger accounts can be identified and corrected	
Differences between the payables ledger and payables ledger control account can be identified and corrected	
To check that irrecoverable debts have been recorded correctly in both the payables ledger and the payables ledger control account	
To ensure that payments made to credit suppliers are recorded correctly in the cash book	

You work in the accounts department of Greaves Limited. Your manager asks you to reconcile the balance of receivables ledger control account to the customers report.

The customers report as at 30 June has been provided:

Customer name	Reference	Balance owed £	Payment terms Days
Bird & Co	BI002	1,344	30
Davenport Ltd	DA001	2,897	30
Gomez Trading	GO001	1,402	30
Mansi Ltd	MA002	3,628	30
Paul & Paul	PA001	7,809	30
Rooke & Co	RO002	4,326	30
Tamayo Ltd	TA001	2,873	30
Unwins	UN001	1,649	30

(b)   **(i)**   If the receivables ledger control account reconciles with the receivables ledger, what will be the balance?

£ _____

The balance on the receivables ledger control account is £26,304.

(ii)   Complete the following statement:

The receivables ledger control account balance is £ [   ] more/less [delete as appropriate] than the receivables ledger.

(c)   The payables ledger control account of Greaves Limited shows a balance of £20,345 but the individual balances in payables ledger add up to £19,462.

Identify whether each of the following may explain the difference between the two balances.

Reason	May explain difference	Does not explain difference
A supplier invoice has been recorded twice in the payables ledger		
The amount for purchases returns has been omitted from payables ledger control account		
A supplier's account balance has been understated when totalling the payables ledger		
A cash purchase has not been recorded in the payables ledger		
A supplier invoice has been recorded in the wrong account in payables ledger		

Task 3

This task is about payment methods and reconciling the cash book to the bank statement.

(a)   Select the most appropriate payment method for each of the following descriptions:

Description	Payment method
A variable date and amount payment set up by the business receiving the payments	
A high value, same-day payment sent through the bank's computer systems	
Simple method used to pay for low-value purchases without using cards or electronic systems	
A bank card payment method used for purchases and cash withdrawals where payment is usually taken from the bank account on the next working day	

Choose from the following payment methods – do not use each more than once:

- BACS
- Cash
- CHAPS
- Cheque

- Credit card
- Debit card
- Direct debit
- Standing order

(b)   A business is reconciling its bank statement to its cash book.

Identify which **one** of the following statements is true.

Statement	
Direct debits paid by the bank are not recorded in the cash book	
At the beginning of each month, the opening balances for the bank statement and the cash book will always be the same	
The bank reconciliation statement makes use of timing differences	

(c)   Identify whether each of the following statements is true or false.

Statement	True	False
The payments column of the bank statement should be checked for automated payments that may have been missed in the cash book		
Where the bank has made an error, the item and amount should not be recorded in the cash book		
When reconciling from the bank statement balance to the cash book balance, unpresented cheques are added		

Task 4

This task is about reconciling a bank statement with the cash book.

The cash book and bank statement for Rafael's business for June 20-4 are shown below.

Cash book

Date 20-4	Details	£	Date 20-4	Cheque number	Details	£
1 June	Balance b/d	13,769	1 June	111043	Prime kitchens	10,000
26 June	Britten & Bond	175	2 June	111044	Long and Lane	80
27 June	Macklin Ltd	950	10 June	111045	BLH Ltd	795
29 June	Randle Fitments	300	11 June	111046	MVR Ltd	652
			12 June	111047	Fairfield Ltd	2,500
			18 June	111048	Makin and King	450
			19 June		LMBC	150
			30 June		Balance c/d	567

Bank statement				
Date 20-4	Description	Paid out £	Paid in £	Balance £
01 June	Balance			15,189 C
03 June	Cheque 111043	10,000		5,189 C
04 June	Cheque 111042	1,420		3,769 C
05 June	Cheque 111044	80		3,689 C
14 June	Cheque 111047	2,500		1,189 C
16 June	BACS Credit: Cairns and Co		571	1,760 C
18 June	Cheque 111045	795		965 C
19 June	Direct Debit: LMBC	150		815 C
28 June	Macklin Ltd		950	1,765 C
29 June	Direct Debit: Insurance Direct	850		915 C
30 June	Bank charges	88		827 C
30 June	Britten & Bond		175	1,002 C
D = Debit C = Credit				

Update the cash book and prepare a bank reconciliation statement at 30 June 20-4.

Select your entries from the following list: Balance b/d, Balance c/d, Bank charges, BLH Ltd, Britten & Bond, Cairns and Co, Fairfield Ltd, Insurance Direct, LMBC, Long and Lane, Macklin Ltd, Makin and King, MVR Ltd, Prime Kitchens, Randle Fitments.

Cash book	Debit	Credit
	£	£
Closing balance b/d	567	
Adjustments:		
Adjusted balance c/d		

Bank reconciliation	£
Closing bank statement balance	1,002
Less unpresented cheques:	
Add outstanding lodgements:	
Adjusted closing cash book balance	

Task 5

This task is about using the journal.

(a)   Identify which **two** of the following situations are a correct use of the journal.

Situation	
Lottie has found an error in the accounting system and wishes to process a journal entry to show how she has corrected the error	
Alice's business has had an excellent week for sales. She wants to record this success through a journal entry	
To increase his capital Ernesto is putting his car into the business. As this is a 'one-off' transaction, he wants to process it through a journal entry	
Blanca has arranged a bank overdraft of £5,000 and her bookkeeper wants to process this through a journal entry	

(b)   A journal entry for payroll transactions is as follows:

30 April 20-1			Journal number: 68
Account name	**Debit**	**Credit**	**Description**
	£	£	
Wages expense	36,451		Gross pay
Bank		30,877	Net pay
Wages expense	2,324		Employer's NIC*
HMRC		2,324	Employer's NIC
HMRC		2,109	Employees' NIC
HMRC		3,465	Income tax (PAYE)

* National Insurance Contributions

Prior to this journal entry, the balance of the HM Revenue & Customs account was debit £255.

After the journal entry is processed, what will be the revised balance owing to HM Revenue & Customs?

£ [   ]

The following invoice has been outstanding for more than six months, and today, 15 December 20-3, Isla wishes to write off the amount as an irrecoverable debt.

Isla's Interiors Ltd
27 Lovell Street, Eveshore EV2 1GH
VAT no 451623031

10 April 20-3   **Invoice no:** 4687

To: Bill's Decorating
18 Tendring Avenue
Eveshore
EV3 9AQ

	£
10 Rolls Wallpaper (design XX3) at £20 per roll	200.00
VAT at 20%	40.00
Total	240.00

Terms: net monthly

(c)   Complete the journal entry below to record the write off of the irrecoverable debt.

15 December 20-3	Journal number: 69		
Account name	**Debit** £	**Credit** £	**Description**
			Write off: irrecoverable debt
			Write off: irrecoverable debt
			Write off: irrecoverable debt

Select your account names from the following list: Bill's Decorating, Irrecoverable debts, Isla's Interiors Ltd, Payables ledger control, Purchases, Receivables ledger control, Sales, Value Added Tax.

Task 6

This task is about using the journal to correct errors.

The trial balance of Kelly's business has disclosed that there are errors – the amount of the imbalance is placed in a suspense account.

(a)   Identify which **two** of the following statements about suspense accounts are true.

Statement	
When errors are disclosed by a trial balance, it is balanced by opening a suspense account for the difference	
A suspense account always has a debit balance	
All errors found within the bookkeeping system are corrected by processing a journal entry, one part of which is an entry for suspense account	
Once errors have been corrected, suspense account has a nil balance and the trial balance can be redrafted	

(b)   Identify whether each of the errors described below would or would not be disclosed by the trial balance.

Error	Disclosed	Not disclosed
The cost of fuel for vehicles has been debited to vehicles account		
Stationery expenses paid from the bank have been debited to both stationery account and bank account		

(c)   Amy and Ben run a retail business. They use a manual accounting system and have prepared a trial balance at the year-end. The trial balance shows total debits of £35,622 and total credits of £36,341.

Amy and Ben have identified the following errors:

Error 1: Business rates paid for August 20-4 of £755 were credited to bank account but were not recorded in business rates account.

Error 2: The day book total of purchases returns for September 20-4 was £684. The amount entered in purchases returns account in the general ledger was £648.

(i)   What is the balance of suspense account in the trial balance?

£ [   ]

This balance is (tick the answer):

Debit	
Credit	

(ii)   Complete the table below with the account names required to show the debits and credits that will be processed through the journal to clear suspense account.

30 September 20-4	Journal number: 175		
Account name	**Debit** £	**Credit** £	**Description**
	755		Correction of error 1
		755	Correction of error 1
	36		Correction of error 2
		36	Correction of error 2

Select your account names from the following list: Balance b/d, Balance c/d, Business rates, Payables ledger control, Purchases, Purchases returns, Receivables ledger control, Sales, Sales returns, Suspense.

Task 7

This task is about extracting a trial balance.

You work in the accounts department at Wickham Limited.

Most of the ledger accounts have been closed off and the balances included in the trial balance at 31 July 20-7.

(a)   You are to complete the remaining ledger accounts by inserting the balance carried down on each account. Enter your answers to two decimal places.

Bank					
20-7	**Details**	**£**	**20-7**	**Details**	**£**
1 Jul	Balance b/d	1,532.98	20 Jul	Stationery	846.95
6 Jul	Sales	2,405.33	25 Jul	Purchases	5,176.27
31 Jul	Receivables ledger control	8,274.19	31 Jul	Payables ledger control	7,465.32
31 Jul	Balance c/d				

Discounts received					
20-7	**Details**	**£**	**20-7**	**Details**	**£**
			1 Jul	Balance b/d	544.63
			31 Jul	Payables ledger control	86.48
31 July	Balance c/d				

Receivables ledger control

20-7	Details	£	20-7	Details	£
1 Jul	Balance b/d	20,353.54	31 Jul	Bank	8,274.19
14 Jul	Sales	6,487.29			
28 Jul	Sales	5,074.68	31 Jul	Balance c/d	

VAT control

20-7	Details	£	20-7	Details	£
31 Jul	Purchases	1,542.61	1 Jul	Balance b/d	978.65
			31 Jul	Sales	2,327.88
31 Jul	Balance c/d				

(b)   Complete the trial balance by inserting the missing figures and calculating the total for each column. Enter your answers to two decimal places.

Item	Debit £	Credit £
Sales		75,591.20
Purchases	60,417.74	
Bank		
Discounts allowed	1,405.19	
Discounts received		
Stationery	6,045.18	
Payables ledger control		12,247.16
Receivables ledger control		
VAT		
Totals		

Task 8

This task is about redrafting a trial balance.

You work in the accounts department at Sutton Supplies. You have been asked to redraft a trial balance after some errors have been identified and the correcting journal entries have been made.

The initial list of balances for Sutton Supplies at 31 March 20-1 is:

Item		£
Sales		86,470.08
Purchases		65,398.34
Discounts allowed		385.62
Bank	debit	12,205.75
Vehicles		28,098.17
Payables ledger control		16,522.84
Suspense	credit	3,094.96

The errors have been identified and the following journal entries need to be processed:

Date: 31 March 20-1		Journal number: 105		
Date	**Description**	**Debit** £	**Credit** £	
31 March	Discounts allowed	45.80		Discounts allowed not recorded in discounts allowed account
31 March	Suspense		45.80	Discounts allowed not recorded in discounts allowed account
31 March	Suspense	3,140.76		Sales of £1,570.38 recorded on debit side of sales account
31 March	Sales		3,140.76	Sales of £1,570.38 recorded on debit side of sales account

You are to complete the adjusted trial balance by inserting the correct figures in either the debit or credit column, and calculating the totals for each column.

Item	Debit £	Credit £
Sales		
Purchases		
Discounts allowed		
Bank		
Vehicles		
Payables ledger control		
Totals		

Practice assessment 2

Assessment information

- This practice assessment contains **8 tasks** and you should attempt to complete **every** task.

- Each task is independent. You will not need to refer to your answers from previous tasks.

- Read every task carefully to make sure you understand what is required.

- Where the date is relevant, it is given in the task data.

- Both minus signs and brackets can be used to indicate negative numbers **unless** task instructions state otherwise.

- You must use a full stop to indicate a decimal point. For example, write 100.57 **not** 100,57 or 10057.

- You may use a comma to indicate a number in the thousands, but you don't have to. For example, 10000 and 10,000 are both acceptable.

- Mathematical rounding should be applied where appropriate.

Task 1

This task is about using control accounts.

A VAT control account balance is shown in general ledger.

(a)   Identify which **one** of the following statements is correct in relation to the VAT control account.

Statement	
VAT on purchases returns is debited to VAT control account	
VAT on discounts received is credited to VAT control account	
The amount of VAT paid to HMRC is credited to VAT control account	
A debit balance on VAT control account shows how much VAT is owing to HMRC	

You work in the accounts department of Elend Limited. Your manager asks you to prepare the receivables ledger control account for July 20-2.

The following information is available for the month of July:

Details	Amount £
Customer balances at 1 July	28,392
Goods sold to credit customers	21,068
Goods returned by credit customers	1,096
Goods sold to cash customers	3,046
Money received from credit customers	22,362
Discounts allowed	492
Irrecoverable debts written off	341

(b) Complete the receivables ledger control account below for July, including the balance carried down at the end of the month.

Receivables ledger control account			
Details	**£**	**Details**	**£**
Balance b/d			
		Balance c/d	

Elend Limited has the following payables ledger control account for July 20-2.

Payables ledger control account					
Date 20-2	**Details**	**£**	**Date 20-2**	**Details**	**£**
31 July	Bank	10,357	1 July	Balance b/d	12,054
31 July	Purchases returns	2,089	31 July	Purchases	15,975
31 July	Discounts received	311			
31 July	Balance c/d				

(c) What is the balance carried down on the payables ledger control account at 31 July 20-2?

£

Task 2

This task is about reconciling control accounts.

The balance of the receivables ledger control account will be used in the year-end trial balance. It is important to reconcile this to the receivables ledger.

(a)   Identify which **one** of the following statements is a reason for completing this reconciliation.

Statement	
Entries made in the wrong receivables ledger accounts can be identified and corrected	
Differences between the receivables ledger and receivables ledger control account can be identified and corrected	
To check that goods sold to cash customers have been recorded correctly in both the receivables ledger and the receivables ledger control account	
To ensure that receipts from credit customers are recorded correctly in the cash book	

You work in the accounts department of Lukac Limited. Your manager asks you to reconcile the balance of payables ledger control account to the suppliers report.

The suppliers report as at 30 September has been provided:

Customer name	Reference	Balance owed £
Albei & Co	AL001	2,104
Dowson Ltd	DO001	1,508
Farr Trading	FA001	696
Manners Ltd	MA001	1,054
Oxley Trading	OX001	248
Patel & Co	PA001	797
Santos Ltd	SA001	3,045
Stanton Ltd	ST001	1,722

(b)   **(i)**   If the payables ledger control account reconciles with the payables ledger, what will be the balance?

£ [   ]

The balance on the payables ledger control account is £11,068.

(ii) Complete the following statement:

The payables ledger control account balance is £ [   ] more/less [delete as appropriate] than the payables ledger.

(c) The receivables ledger control account of Lukac Limited shows a balance of £18,475 but the individual balances in receivables ledger add up to £17,348.

Identify whether each of the following may explain the difference between the two balances.

Reason	May explain difference	Does not explain difference
A customer invoice has been recorded twice in the receivables ledger		
The amount for sales returns has been omitted from receivables ledger control account		
A customer's account balance has been overstated when totalling the receivables ledger		
A cash sale has not been recorded in the receivables ledger		
A customer invoice has been recorded in the wrong account in receivables ledger		

Task 3

This task is about payment methods and reconciling the cash book to the bank statement.

(a) Select the most appropriate payment method for each of the following descriptions:

Description	Payment method
Regular fixed date payments for the same amount set up with the bank by the business sending the money	
Computer-based direct payments between bank accounts with a three day clearance	
An instruction in writing, signed by the bank's customer, telling the bank to pay a one-off amount to a named person	
A card issued on a 'buy now and pay later' basis and for cash withdrawals; payment is made monthly in full or in part	

Choose from the following payment methods – do not use each more than once:

- BACS
- Cash
- CHAPS
- Cheque

- Credit card
- Debit card
- Direct debit
- Standing order

(b) A business is reconciling its bank statement to its cash book.

Identify which **one** of the following statements is true.

Statement	
Unpresented cheques are timing differences which need to be deducted in the cash book	
A completed bank reconciliation statement proves that there are no errors in the accounting system	
Faster Payments receipts shown on the bank statement need to be recorded in the cash book	

(c) Identify whether each of the following statements is true or false.

Statement	True	False
A direct debit payment recorded on the bank statement but not in the cash book is deducted on the bank reconciliation statement		
Outstanding lodgements are amounts paid into the bank but not yet recorded on the bank statement		
A credit balance on a bank statement is a debit balance in a business cash book		

Task 4

This task is about reconciling a bank statement with the cash book.

The cash book and bank statement for Imogen's business for May 20-2 are shown below.

Cash book

Date 20-2	Details	£	Date 20-2	Cheque number	Details	£
1 May	Balance b/d	177	1 May	114118	Harrop & Co	395
5 May	Cottle Ltd	4,806	10 May	114119	Farr Ltd	2,218
20 May	W Waugh	2,108	20 May	114120	Bradnock Traders	1,036
29 May	Pardo Ltd	1,746	20 May	114121	Paxtons	1,427
30 May	Torre & Co	542	21 May	114122	Filiaps Ltd	798
			21 May		Wyvern Council	235
					Balance c/d	3,270

Bank statement

Date 20-2	Description	Paid out £	Paid in £	Balance £
01 May	Balance			1,487 C
04 May	Cheque 114118	395		1,092 C
05 May	Cheque 114117	1,310		218 D
05 May	BACS Credit: Cottle Ltd		4,806	4,588 C
18 May	Cheque 114119	2,218		2,370 C
21 May	Direct Debit: Wyvern Council	235		2,135 C
21 May	BACS Credit: Bayer Ltd		1,095	3,230 C
21 May	BACS Credit: Allen plc		2,786	6,016 C
22 May	Direct Debit: JA Finance	592		5,424 C
22 May	Cheque 114121	1,427		3,997 C
24 May	Cheque: W Waugh		2,108	6,105 C
28 May	Bank charges	45		6,060 C
D = Debit C = Credit				

Update the cash book and prepare a bank reconciliation statement at 31 May 20-2.

Select your entries from the following list: Allen plc, Balance b/d, Balance c/d, Bank charges, Bayer Ltd, Bradnock Traders, Cottle Ltd, Farr Ltd, Filiaps Ltd, Harrop & Co, JA Finance, Pardo Ltd, Paxtons, Torre & Co, W Waugh, Wyvern Council.

Cash book	Debit	Credit
	£	£
Closing balance b/d	3,270	
Adjustments:		
Adjusted balance c/d		

Bank reconciliation	£
Closing bank statement balance	6,060
Less unpresented cheques:	
Add outstanding lodgements:	
Adjusted closing cash book balance	

Task 5

This task is about using the journal.

(a) Identify which **two** of the following situations are a correct use of the journal.

Situation	
Arthur has a new bookkeeper who has prepared the monthly payroll transactions	
Alexandra runs a delicatessen and she has bought goods for resale on credit from Kernow Cheese Ltd	
Emma has taken cash drawings from her business	
Faye's bookkeeper has found an error in the accounts which needs to be corrected	

(b) Jon is setting up in business and has asked you to prepare his opening journal entry. He is starting his business with cash £250, bank £4,500, inventory £2,500, office equipment £2,850, payables £725.

Complete the opening journal entry for his business as at 1 May 20-6.

1 May 20-6	Journal number: 001	
Account name	**Debit** £	**Credit** £
Totals		

(c) The following invoice has been outstanding for more than six months, and today, 10 December 20-2, Lena wishes to make a journal entry to write off the amount as an irrecoverable debt.

Lena's Lighting Supplies
18 High Street, Wyvern WV1 7PP
VAT no 457321849

4 March 20-2   **Invoice no:** 3471

To: Oxley Electricians
22 London Road
Wyvern
WV2 3QR

	£
2 'Olympus' light fittings at £125 each	250.00
VAT at 20%	50.00
Total	300.00

Terms: net monthly

Prior to writing off this debt, the balance of irrecoverable debts account was debit £295.

After the journal entry is processed, what will be the revised balance on irrecoverable debts account? Indicate whether the revised balance is debit or credit.

£ [ ] | Debit / Credit |

Task 6

This task is about using the journal to correct errors.

The trial balance of Eve's business has disclosed that there are errors – the amount of the imbalance is placed in a suspense account.

(a)   Identify which **two** of the following statements about suspense accounts are true.

Statement	
When the debit side total of a trial balance is more than the credit side total, a suspense account is opened with a debit balance	
The correction of errors not disclosed by the trial balance are recorded through suspense account	
After errors disclosed by the trial balance have been corrected, a redrafted trial balance will show that suspense has been cleared	
A suspense account can have either a debit balance or a credit balance	

(b)   Identify whether each of the errors described below would or would not be disclosed by the trial balance.

Error	Disclosed	Not disclosed
Fuel for vehicles of £55 has been debited to vehicles account		
Rent paid account has been overcast by £100		

(c)   Olga and Nisha run a retail business. They use a manual accounting system and have prepared a year-end trial balance at 30 April 20-5. The trial balance shows total debits of £42,854 and total credits of £42,095.

Olga and Nisha have identified the following errors:

Error 1: Rent received of £750 (no VAT) for April 20-5 has been entered in bank account but was not recorded in rent received account.

Error 2: The day book total of sales returns for April 20-5 was £512. The amount entered in sales returns account in the general ledger was £521.

(i)   What is the balance of suspense account in the trial balance?

£ [   ]

This balance is (tick the answer):

Debit	
Credit	

(ii) Complete the table below with the account names required to show the debits and credits that will be processed through the journal to clear suspense account.

30 April 20-5	Journal number: 314		
Account name	**Debit** £	**Credit** £	**Description**
			Correction of error 1 Correction of error 1
			Correction of error 2 Correction of error 2

Select your account names from the following list: Balance b/d, Balance c/d, Payables ledger control, Purchases, Purchases returns, Receivables ledger control, Rent received, Sales, Sales returns, Suspense.

Task 7

This task is about extracting a trial balance.

You work in the accounts department at Chazel Limited.

Most of the ledger accounts have been closed off and the balances included in the year-end trial balance at 30 June 20-8.

(a) You are to complete the remaining ledger accounts by inserting the balance carried down on each account. Enter your answers to two decimal places.

Bank					
20-8	**Details**	**£**	**20-8**	**Details**	**£**
1 Jun	Balance b/d	856.92	15 Jun	Office expenses	2,528.88
30 Jun	Capital	5,210.63	20 Jun	Purchases	3,045.22
30 Jun	Receivables ledger control	18,428.15	30 Jun	Payables ledger control	10,247.91
			30 Jun	Balance c/d	

Office expenses					
20-8	**Details**	**£**	**20-8**	**Details**	**£**
1 Jun	Balance b/d	10,504.68			
15 Jun	Bank	2,107.40			
			30 Jun	Balance c/d	

Payables ledger control					
20-8	**Details**	**£**	**20-8**	**Details**	**£**
30 Jun	Bank	10,247.91	1 Jun	Balance b/d	18,328.14
			10 Jun	Purchases	5,329.02
30 Jun	Balance c/d		28 Jun	Purchases	7,063.14

Capital					
20-8	**Details**	**£**	**20-8**	**Details**	**£**
30 Jun	Bank	1,810.95	1 Jun	Balance b/d	13,715.88
30 Jun	Balance c/d				

(b) Complete the trial balance by inserting the missing figures and calculating the total for each column. Enter your answers to two decimal places.

Item	Debit £	Credit £
Sales		115,350.13
Purchases	86,024.28	
Bank		
Discounts allowed	828.44	
Capital		
Office expenses		
Payables ledger control		
Receivables ledger control	42,106.11	
VAT		2,517.15
Totals		

Task 8

This task is about redrafting a trial balance.

You work in the accounts department at Excel Electrical Supplies. You have been asked to redraft a trial balance after some errors have been identified and the correcting journal entries have been made.

The initial list of balances for Excel Electrical Supplies at 30 September 20-4 is:

Item		£
Sales		75,292.84
Purchases		66,810.13
Sales returns		680.20
Bank	debit	11,266.95
Receivables ledger control		25,271.16
Payables ledger control		20,310.18
Capital		8,310.69
Suspense	credit	114.73

The errors have been identified and the following journal entries need to be processed:

Date: 30 September 20-1		Journal number: 86		
Date	**Description**	**Debit** £	**Credit** £	
30 Sept	Suspense	445.13		Sales not recorded in sales account
30 Sept	Sales		445.13	Sales not recorded in sales account
30 Sept	Sales returns	330.40		Sales returns of £165.20 recorded on credit side of sales returns account
30 Sept	Suspense		330.40	Sales returns of £165.20 recorded on credit side of sales returns account

You are to complete the adjusted trial balance by inserting the correct figures in either the debit or credit column, and calculating the totals for each column.

Item	Debit £	Credit £
Sales		
Purchases		
Sales returns		
Bank		
Receivables ledger control		
Payables ledger control		
Capital		
Totals		

Practice assessment 3

Assessment information

- This practice assessment contains **8 tasks** and you should attempt to complete **every** task.

- Each task is independent. You will not need to refer to your answers from previous tasks.

- Read every task carefully to make sure you understand what is required.

- Where the date is relevant, it is given in the task data.

- Both minus signs and brackets can be used to indicate negative numbers **unless** task instructions state otherwise.

- You must use a full stop to indicate a decimal point. For example, write 100.57 **not** 100,57 or 10057.

- You may use a comma to indicate a number in the thousands, but you don't have to. For example, 10000 and 10,000 are both acceptable.

- Mathematical rounding should be applied where appropriate.

Task 1

This task is about using control accounts.

(a)   Identify whether each of the following statements is true or false.

Statement	True	False
A debit balance on VAT control account shows how much is due from HMRC		
Discounts received is recorded on the credit side of payables ledger control account		

(b)   You are an Accounts Assistant at Wembley Wines Ltd. Today you are working on the control accounts.

The balance of receivables ledger control account at 1 April 20-2 is £15,043.

You have printed a report for April from the accounting system with the following information:

Details: April 20-2	Total £	VAT £	Net £
Sales day book	14,448	2,408	12,040
Sales returns day book	1,116	186	930
Discounts allowed day book	252	42	210
Bank – receipts from credit customers	13,200		

Complete the table below for the month to show the entries in the receivables ledger control account and the balance at 30 April. Ensure numbers are included in either the debit or credit column.

Receivables ledger control	Debit £	Credit £
1 April 20-2 Balance b/d		
Sales day book		
Sales returns day book		
Discounts allowed day book		
Bank – receipts from credit customers		
30 April 20-2 Balance c/d		

The balance of VAT control account at 1 April 20-2 is £2,346 credit.

You have printed a report for April from the accounting system with the following information:

Details: April 20-2	Total £
VAT on sales	2,408
VAT on purchases	1,743
VAT on discounts allowed	42
VAT on sales returns	186
Bank – payment to HMRC	1,027

During the month there were no purchases returns, no discounts received, and no cash sales or purchases.

Calculate the balance brought down on the VAT control account at 1 May 20-2.

£ [   ]   Debit [   ]   Credit [   ]

Task 2

This task is about reconciling control accounts.

(a) Complete the following statements about control accounts by selecting the correct options to complete the gaps.

An entry made in the wrong receivables ledger account ....[GAP 1]............ be revealed by the receivables ledger control account.
Reconciling the payables ledger control account to the payables ledger could reveal errors in ....[GAP 2]........................

GAP 1 OPTIONS
will
will not

GAP 2 OPTIONS
payables ledger only
payables ledger control account only
both payables ledger and payables ledger control account

(b) You are an Accounts Assistant at Nord Foods Ltd.

The following supplier accounts make up the payables ledger at 1 September 20-6.

Brocken Ltd

Details	Amount £	Details	Amount £
		Balance b/d	7,328

Annan plc

Details	Amount £	Details	Amount £
		Balance b/d	4,111

Elend & Sons

Details	Amount £	Details	Amount £
Balance b/d	384		

White and Hart

Details	Amount £	Details	Amount £
		Balance b/d	5,176

(i)   What is the total of the balances in the payables ledger at 1 September 20-6?

£ [   ]

(ii)   The balance on the payables ledger control account on 1 September 20-6 is £15,646.

What is the difference between the balance on the payables ledger control account and the total of the balances in the payables ledger?

£ [   ]

(iii)   Which **two** of the reasons below could explain the difference you calculated in (ii)?

Reasons	
Purchases were entered twice in a supplier's account in the payables ledger	
Purchases returns were not entered in the payables ledger control account	
Purchases returns were entered twice in a supplier's account in the payables ledger	
Discounts received were not entered in the payables ledger control account	
A bank payment to a supplier was entered into the wrong supplier's account in the payables ledger	
A bank payment to a supplier was entered twice in the payables ledger control account	

Task 3

This task is about payment methods and reconciling the cash book to the bank statement.

(a)   Identify whether the following payment methods are debited to the bank account immediately (same day) or at a later date.

Payment method	Immediate	Later date
Faster payment		
Debit card		

(b)   Identify the type of difference between the cash book and the bank statement for each of the descriptions below.

Description	Difference
A cheque from a customer, which was entered in the cash book and paid into the bank last week, has been returned	
Cheques to suppliers have been recorded in the cash book, but are not yet shown on the bank statement	
The monthly payment for business rates has been made automatically by the bank	
Cash and cheques from customers were recorded in the cash book and paid into the bank today, but are not yet shown on the bank statement	

Choose your differences from the following options:

Outstanding lodgements
Unpresented cheques
Unpaid cheques
Direct debit
Bank charges
Counter credit

(c)   Identify whether the following adjustments will need to be made in the cash book or the bank reconciliation statement.

Adjustment	Cash book	Bank reconciliation
Bank charges are deducted on the bank statement		
Cash sales recorded in the cash book are not shown on the bank statement		

Task 4

This task is about reconciling a bank statement with the cash book.

The cash book and bank statement for Holly's business for September 20-4 are shown below.

Cash book

Date 20-4	Details	£	Date 20-4	Cheque number	Details	£
4 Sep	Green & Co	2,307	1 Sep		Balance b/d	1,376
13 Sep	Peer Prints	653	6 Sep	112002	Ace Timber	186
20 Sep	Bristows	742	9 Sep	112003	Fairfield Ltd	870
29 Sep	Barber & Bates	469	13 Sep	112004	BLH Ltd	219
30 Sep	Jackson & Co	245	24 Sep	112005	Bridge Tools	607
30 Sep	Balance c/d	947	26 Sep		A-Z Finance	600
			28 Sep	112006	Tenon Ltd	1,505

Bank statement				
Date 20-4	Description	Paid out £	Paid in £	Balance £
01 Sep	Balance			252 C
02 Sep	Cheque 112001	1,628		1,376 D
04 Sep	BACS credit: Green & Co		2,307	931 C
08 Sep	Cheque 112002	186		745 C
12 Sep	Cheque 112003	870		125 D
13 Sep	BACS credit: Peer Prints		653	528 C
18 Sep	Cheque 112004	219		309 C
20 Sep	Counter credit: Bristows		742	1,051 C
26 Sep	Direct Debit: A-Z Finance	600		451 C
28 Sep	BACS credit: GTK Ltd		349	800 C
30 Sep	Bank charges	148		652 C
D = Debit C = Credit				

Update the cash book and prepare a bank reconciliation statement at 30 September 20-4.

Select your entries from the following list: Ace Timber, A-Z Finance, Balance b/d, Balance c/d, Bank charges, Barber & Bates, BLH Ltd, Bridge Tools, Fairfield Ltd, Green & Co, GTK Ltd, Jackson & Co, Peer Prints, Tenon Ltd.

Cash book	Debit £	Credit £
Closing balance b/d		947
Adjustments:		
Adjusted balance c/d		

Bank reconciliation	£
Closing bank statement balance	652
Less unpresented cheques:	
Add outstanding lodgements:	
Adjusted closing cash book balance	

Task 5

This task is about using the journal.

(a)   Julia is in business selling artists' materials from a shop which she rents. She has produced accounts using a spreadsheet up until 1 January 20-6 but now wishes to start using a cloud accounting system.

She has the following items which are to be included as opening balances in the new accounting system: cash £320, bank overdraft £585, inventory £3,250, shop fittings £2,650, payables £1,050.

Complete the opening journal entry for her business as at 1 January 20-6.

1 January 20-6	Journal number: 001	
Account name	**Debit** £	**Credit** £
Cash		
Bank		
Inventory		
Shop fittings		
Payables		
Capital		
Totals		

(b)   Lottie runs a gardening business, which is registered for VAT. She has recorded the following journal entry in her accounting system at her year-end of 30 June 20-5:

30 June 20-5		Journal number: 54	
Account name	**Debit** £	**Credit** £	**Description**
Receivables ledger control		180	Write off: irrecoverable debt
Irrecoverable debts	150		Write off: irrecoverable debt
Value Added Tax	30		Write off: irrecoverable debt

The receivables ledger control account has a closing balance before processing this journal entry of £2,508 debit.

After the journal is processed, what will be the revised balance carried down on her receivables ledger control account?

£ [   ]

(c) Greta employs six people in her business. At 30 April 20-8 she needs to prepare a journal to reflect the following payroll information for the month:

Gross pay £7,800

Income tax £760

Employees' National Insurance Contributions (NIC) £450

Employer's National Insurance Contributions (NIC) £520

Complete the journal entry for her payroll transactions.

30 April 20-8	Journal number: 75	
Account name	**Debit** £	**Credit** £
Wages expense		
HMRC – Income tax		
HMRC – NIC		
Net wages		
Totals		

Task 6

This task is about using the journal to correct errors.

(a)   Identify the type of error not disclosed by the trial balance which is described by each of the following statements. Choose from the types of error listed in the option box below.

Statement	Type of error
Tom has paid for repairs to his delivery van. He has coded the cost to his vehicles account	
Alice has coded rent paid on her business premises to her stationery account	
Daisy has bought copy paper for use in the office and paid in cash. She has forgotten to record the entry in her accounting system	
Ernesto has bought a computer for his business. He has coded it as a debit to bank account and a credit to office equipment account	

OPTIONS
Error of omission
Error of commission
Error of principle
Error of original entry
Reversal of entries
Compensating error

(b)   Ravi is in business as a repairer of domestic kitchen appliances.

On 30 June 20-7 his bookkeeper prepared a trial balance which did not balance. The debit column totalled £156,966 and the credit column totalled £155,521.

(i)   What entry is needed in the suspense account to balance the trial balance?

Account name	Debit £	Credit £
Suspense		

(ii) The journal entries to correct all the bookkeeping errors, and a list of balances as they appear in the trial balance, are shown below.

30 June 20-7	Journal number: 68	
Account name	Debit £	Credit £
Office stationery	355	
Suspense		355
Suspense	1,800	
Rent received		1,800
Delivery expenses	450	
Bank		450

Complete the table below to show:

• the balance of each account after the journal entries have been recorded

• whether each balance will be a debit or credit entry in the trial balance

Account name	Original balance £	New balance £	Debit in trial balance	Credit in trial balance
Office stationery	3,027			
Rent received	8,040			
Delivery expenses	1,285			
Bank (overdraft)	3,261			

(c) Maggie's trial balance fails to agree by £125 and the difference is placed in a suspense account. Later it is found that a cash purchase for this amount has not been recorded in the purchases account. Which **one** of the following journal entries is correct?

Debit suspense account £125; credit purchases account £125	
Debit purchases account £250; credit suspense account £250	
Debit purchases account £125; credit suspense account £125	
Debit purchases account £125	

Task 7

This task is about extracting a trial balance.

You work in the accounts department at Oxley Limited.

Most of the ledger accounts have been closed off and the balances included in the year-end trial balance at 31 December 20-8.

(a)   You are to complete the remaining ledger accounts by inserting the balance carried down on each account. Enter your answers to two decimal places.

Office equipment						
20-8	**Details**	**£**	**20-8**	**Details**		**£**
1 Dec	Balance b/d	22,250.00				
10 Dec	Bank	1,700.00				
			31 Dec	Balance c/d		

Purchases returns						
20-8	**Details**	**£**	**20-8**	**Details**		**£**
			1 Dec	Balance b/d		358.26
			15 Dec	Payables ledger control		176.52
31 Dec	Balance c/d					

Receivables ledger control						
20-8	**Details**	**£**	**20-8**	**Details**		**£**
1 Dec	Balance b/d	12,582.36	10 Dec	Irrecoverable debt		146.29
31 Dec	Sales	7,054.18	31 Dec	Sales returns		278.84
			31 Dec	Bank		7,052.13
			31 Dec	Balance c/d		

Capital						
20-8	**Details**	**£**	**20-8**	**Details**		**£**
31 Dec	Bank	1,890.50	1 Dec	Balance b/d		36,200.00
31 Dec	Balance c/d					

(b) Complete the trial balance by inserting the missing figures and calculating the total for each column. Enter your answers to two decimal places.

Item	Debit £	Credit £
Sales		120,452.18
Purchases	86,422.76	
Purchases returns		
Bank	40,581.18	
Irrecoverable debts	480.29	
Capital		
Office equipment		
Payables ledger control		7,054.92
Receivables ledger control		
VAT		1,242.13
Totals		

Task 8

This task is about redrafting a trial balance.

You work in the accounts department at Vernon Ltd. You have been asked to redraft a trial balance after some errors have been identified and the correcting journal entries have been made.

The initial list of balances Vernon Ltd at 31 March 20-2 is:

Item		£
Sales		42,308.16
Purchases		39,107.38
Irrecoverable debts		320.21
Bank	debit	9,332.66
Receivables ledger control		14,760.84
Payables ledger control		10,108.76
Capital		14,092.36
Wages		3,064.96

The errors have been identified and the following journal entries need to be processed:

Date: 30 March 20-2		Journal number: 104		
Date	**Description**	**Debit** £	**Credit** £	
31 March	Suspense	272.15		Cash sales not coded
31 March	Sales		272.15	Cash sales not coded
31 March	Irrecoverable debts	195.38		Irrecoverable debt not initially coded
31 March	Suspense		195.38	Irrecoverable debt not initially coded

You are to complete the adjusted trial balance by inserting the correct figures in either the debit or credit column, and calculating the totals for each column.

Item	Debit £	Credit £
Sales		
Purchases		
Irrecoverable debts		
Bank		
Receivables ledger control		
Payables ledger control		
Capital		
Wages		
Totals		

Answers to practice assessment 1

Task 1

(a)

Statement	
An entry made in the wrong receivables ledger account will be revealed by the receivables ledger control account	
The net figure from sales day book is debited to receivables ledger control account	
Irrecoverable debts written off are not recorded in receivables ledger control account	
The balance of receivables ledger control account gives a total figure for the amount owing by credit customers	✔

(b)

VAT control account			
Details	**£**	**Details**	**£**
Purchases	1,345	Balance b/d	1,585
Sales returns	205	Sales	2,627
Discounts allowed	122	Purchases returns	286
Bank	1,585	Discounts received	154
		Cash sales	728
Balance c/d	2,123		

(c)   £ | 9,205 |

Task 2

(a)

Statement	
Entries made in the wrong payables ledger accounts can be identified and corrected	
Differences between the payables ledger and payables ledger control account can be identified and corrected	✔
To check that irrecoverable debts have been recorded correctly in both the payables ledger and the payables ledger control account	
To ensure that payments made to credit suppliers are recorded correctly in the cash book	

(b) **(i)** £ | 25,928

(ii) The receivables ledger control account balance is £ | 376 | more than the receivables ledger.

(c)

Reason	May explain difference	Does not explain difference
A supplier invoice has been recorded twice in the payables ledger		✔
The amount for purchases returns has been omitted from payables ledger control account	✔	
A supplier's account balance has been understated when totalling the payables ledger	✔	
A cash purchase has not been recorded in the payables ledger		✔
A supplier invoice has been recorded in the wrong account in payables ledger		✔

Task 3

(a)

Description	Payment method
A variable date and amount payment set up by the business receiving the payments	Direct debit
A high value, same-day payment sent through the banks' computer systems	CHAPS
Simple method used to pay for low-value purchases without using cards or electronic systems	Cash
A bank card payment method used for purchases and cash withdrawals where payment is usually taken from the bank account on the next working day	Debit card

(b)

Statement	
Direct debits paid by the bank are not recorded in the cash book	
At the beginning of each month the opening balances for the bank statement and the cash book will always be the same	
The bank reconciliation statement makes use of timing differences	✔

(c)

Statement	True	False
The payments column of the bank statement should be checked for automated payments that may have been missed in the cash book	✔	
Where the bank has made an error, the item and amount should not be recorded in the cash book	✔	
When reconciling from the bank statement balance to the cash book balance, unpresented cheques are added		✔

Task 4

Cash book	Debit £	Credit £
Closing balance b/d	567	
Adjustments:		
Cairns and Co	571	
Insurance Direct		850
Bank charges		88
Adjusted balance c/d		200

Bank reconciliation	£
Closing bank statement balance	1,002
Less unpresented cheques:	
MVR Ltd	652
Makin and King	450
Add outstanding lodgements:	
Randle Fitments	300
Adjusted closing cash book balance	200

Task 5

(a)

Situation	
Lottie has found an error in the accounting system and wishes to process a journal entry to show how she has corrected the error	✔
Alice's business has had an excellent week for sales. She wants to record this success through a journal entry	
To increase his capital Ernesto is putting his car into the business. As this is a 'one-off' transaction, he wants to process it through a journal entry	✔
Blanca has arranged a bank overdraft of £5,000 and her bookkeeper wants to process this through a journal entry	

(b) £ 7,643

(c)

15 December 20-3		Journal number: 69	
Account name	**Debit** £	**Credit** £	**Description**
Receivables ledger control		240	Write off: irrecoverable debt
Irrecoverable debts	200		Write off: irrecoverable debt
Value Added Tax	40		Write off: irrecoverable debt

Task 6

(a)

Statement	
When errors are disclosed by a trial balance, it is balanced by opening a suspense account for the difference	✔
A suspense account always has a debit balance	
All errors found within the bookkeeping system are corrected by processing a journal entry, one part of which is an entry for suspense account	
Once errors have been corrected, suspense account has a nil balance and the trial balance can be redrafted	✔

(b)

Error	Disclosed	Not disclosed
The cost of fuel for vehicles has been debited to vehicles account		✔
Stationery expenses paid from the bank have been debited to both stationery account and bank account	✔	

(c) **(i)** £ | 719 |

Debit	✔
Credit	

(ii)

30 September 20-4	Journal number: 175		
Account name	**Debit** £	**Credit** £	**Description**
Business rates	755		Correction of error 1
Suspense		755	Correction of error 1
Suspense	36		Correction of error 2
Purchases returns		36	Correction of error 2

Tutorial note: the difference of £36 has been entered here. An alternative treatment is to take out the wrong figure of £648 (debit purchases returns; credit suspense) and then record the correct figure of £684 (debit suspense; credit purchases returns). The effect is the same as the net amount of £36 shown above.

Task 7

(a)

Bank						
20-7	**Details**	**£**	**20-7**	**Details**		**£**
1 Jul	Balance b/d	1,532.98	20 Jul	Stationery		846.95
6 Jul	Sales	2,405.33	25 Jul	Purchases		5,176.27
31 Jul	Receivables ledger control	8,274.19	31 Jul	Payables ledger control		7,465.32
31 Jul	Balance c/d	1,276.04				

Discounts received

20-7	Details	£	20-7	Details	£
			1 Jul	Balance b/d	544.63
			31 Jul	Payables ledger control	86.48
31 July	Balance c/d	631.11			

Receivables ledger control

20-7	Details	£	20-7	Details	£
1 Jul	Balance b/d	20,353.54	31 Jul	Bank	8,274.19
14 Jul	Sales	6,487.29			
28 Jul	Sales	5,074.68	31 Jul	Balance c/d	23,641.32

VAT control

20-7	Details	£	20-7	Details	£
31 Jul	Purchases	1,542.61	1 Jul	Balance b/d	978.65
			31 Jul	Sales	2,327.88
31 Jul	Balance c/d	1,763.92			

(b)

Item	Debit £	Credit £
Sales		75,591.20
Purchases	60,417.74	
Bank		1,276.04
Discounts allowed	1,405.19	
Discounts received		631.11
Stationery	6,045.18	
Payables ledger control		12,247.16
Receivables ledger control	23,641.32	
VAT control		1,763.92
Totals	91,509.43	91,509.43

Task 8

Item	Debit £	Credit £
Sales		89,610.84
Purchases	65,398.34	
Discounts allowed	431.42	
Bank	12,205.75	
Vehicles	28,098.17	
Payables ledger control		16,522.84
Totals	106,133.68	106,133.68

Answers to practice assessment 2

Task 1

(a)

Statement	
VAT on purchases returns is debited to VAT control account	
VAT on discounts received is credited to VAT control account	✔
The amount of VAT paid to HMRC is credited to VAT control account	
A debit balance on VAT control account shows how much VAT is owing to HMRC	

(b)

Receivables ledger control account			
Details	**£**	**Details**	**£**
Balance b/d	28,392	Sales returns	1,096
Sales	21,068	Bank	22,362
		Discounts allowed	492
		Irrecoverable debts	341
		Balance c/d	25,169

(c)   £ | 15,272 |

Task 2

(a)

Statement	
Entries made in the wrong receivables ledger accounts can be identified and corrected	
Differences between the receivables ledger and receivables ledger control account can be identified and corrected	✔
To check that goods sold to cash customers have been recorded correctly in both the receivables ledger and the receivables ledger control account	
To ensure that receipts from credit customers are recorded correctly in the cash book	

(b) **(i)** £ | 11,174 |

(ii) The payables ledger control account balance is £ | 106 | less than the payables ledger.

(c)

Reason	May explain difference	Does not explain difference
A customer invoice has been recorded twice in the receivables ledger		✔
The amount for sales returns has been omitted from receivables ledger control account	✔	
A customer's account balance has been overstated when totalling the receivables ledger		✔
A cash sale has not been recorded in the receivables ledger		✔
A customer invoice has been recorded in the wrong account in receivables ledger		✔

Task 3

(a)

Description	Payment method
Regular fixed date payments for the same amount set up with the bank by the business sending the money	Standing order
Computer-based direct payments between bank accounts with a three day clearance	BACS
An instruction in writing, signed by the bank's customer, telling the bank to pay a one-off amount to a named person	Cheque
A card issued on a 'buy now and pay later' basis and for cash withdrawals; payment is made monthly in full or in part	Credit card

(b)

Statement	
Unpresented cheques are timing differences which need to be deducted in the cash book	
A completed bank reconciliation statement proves that there are no errors in the accounting system	
Faster Payments receipts shown on the bank statement need to be recorded in the cash book	✔

(c)

Statement	True	False
A direct debit payment recorded on the bank statement but not in the cash book is deducted on the bank reconciliation statement		✔
Outstanding lodgements are amounts paid into the bank but not yet recorded on the bank statement	✔	
A credit balance on a bank statement is a debit balance in a business cash book	✔	

Task 4

Cash Book	Debit	Credit
	£	£
Closing balance b/d	3,270	
Adjustments:		
Bayer Ltd	1,095	
Allen plc	2,786	
JA Finance		592
Bank charges		45
Adjusted balance c/d		6,514

Bank reconciliation	£
Closing bank statement balance	6,060
Less unpresented cheques:	
Bradnock Traders	1,036
Filiaps Ltd	798
Add outstanding lodgements:	
Pardo Ltd	1,746
Torre & Co	542
Adjusted closing cash book balance	6,514

Task 5

(a)

Situation	
Arthur has a new bookkeeper who has prepared the monthly payroll transactions.	✔
Alexandra runs a delicatessen and she has bought goods for resale on credit from Kernow Cheese Ltd.	
Emma has taken cash drawings from her business.	
Faye's bookkeeper has found an error in the accounts which needs to be corrected.	✔

(b)

1 May 20-6		Journal number: 001	
Account name	**Debit £**		**Credit £**
Cash	250		
Bank	4,500		
Inventory	2,500		
Office equipment	2,850		
Payables			725
Capital			9,375
Totals	10,100		10,100

(c)   £ 545   Debit / ~~Credit~~

Task 6

(a)

Statement	
When the debit side total of a trial balance is more than the credit side total, a suspense account is opened with a debit balance	
The correction of errors not disclosed by the trial balance are recorded through suspense account	
After errors disclosed by the trial balance have been corrected, a redrafted trial balance will show that suspense has been cleared	✔
A suspense account can have either a debit balance or a credit balance	✔

(b)

Error	Disclosed	Not disclosed
Fuel for vehicles of £55 has been debited to vehicles account		✔
Rent paid account has been overcast by £100	✔	

(c) **(i)**   £ | 759 |

Debit	
Credit	✔

(ii)

30 April 20-5	Journal number: 314		
Account name	**Debit** £	**Credit** £	**Description**
Suspense	750		Correction of error 1
Rent received		750	Correction of error 1
Suspense	9		Correction of error 2
Sales returns		9	Correction of error 2

Task 7

(a)

Bank					
20-8	**Details**	**£**	**20-8**	**Details**	**£**
1 Jun	Balance b/d	856.92	15 Jun	Office expenses	2,528.88
30 Jun	Capital	5,210.63	20 Jun	Purchases	3,045.22
30 Jun	Receivables ledger control	18,428.15	30 Jun	Payables ledger control	10,247.91
			30 Jun	Balance c/d	8,673.69

Office expenses					
20-8	**Details**	**£**	**20-8**	**Details**	**£**
1 Jun	Balance b/d	10,504.68			
15 Jun	Bank	2,107.40			
			30 Jun	Balance c/d	12,612.08

Payables ledger control					
20-8	**Details**	**£**	**20-8**	**Details**	**£**
30 Jun	Bank	10,247.91	1 Jun	Balance b/d	18,328.14
			10 Jun	Purchases	5,329.02
30 Jun	Balance c/d	20,472.39	28 Jun	Purchases	7,063.14

Capital					
20-8	**Details**	**£**	**20-8**	**Details**	**£**
30 Jun	Bank	1,810.95	1 Jun	Balance b/d	13,715.88
30 Jun	Balance c/d	11,904.93			

(b)

Item	Debit £	Credit £
Sales		115,350.13
Purchases	86,024.28	
Bank	8,673.69	
Discounts allowed	828.44	
Capital		11,904.93
Office expenses	12,612.08	
Payables ledger control		20,472.39
Receivables ledger control	42,106.11	
VAT control		2,517.15
Totals	150,244.60	150,244.60

Task 8

Item	Debit £	Credit £
Sales		75,737.97
Purchases	66,810.13	
Sales returns	1,010.60	
Bank	11,266.95	
Receivables ledger control	25,271.16	
Payables ledger control		20,310.18
Capital		8,310.69
Totals	104,358.84	104,358.84

Answers to practice assessment 3

Task 1

(a)

Statement	True	False
A debit balance on VAT control account shows how much is due from HMRC	✔	
Discounts received is recorded on the credit side of payables ledger control account		✔

(b)

Receivables ledger control	Debit £	Credit £
1 April 20-2 Balance b/d	15,043	
Sales day book	14,448	
Sales returns day book		1,116
Discounts allowed day book		252
Bank – receipts from credit customers		13,200
30 April 20-2 Balance c/d		14,923

£ | 1,756 | Debit | | Credit | ✔ |

Task 2

(a)

An entry made in the wrong receivables ledger account **will not** be revealed by the receivables ledger control account.
Reconciling the payables ledger control account to the payables ledger could reveal errors in **both payables ledger and payables ledger control account.**

(b)   **(i)**   £ | 16,231 |

        (ii)   £ | 585 |

(iii)

Reasons	
Purchases were entered twice in a supplier's account in the payables ledger	✔
Purchases returns were not entered in the payables ledger control account	
Purchases returns were entered twice in a supplier's account in the payables ledger	
Discounts received were not entered in the payables ledger control account	
A bank payment to a supplier was entered into the wrong supplier's account in the payables ledger	
A bank payment to a supplier was entered twice in the payables ledger control account	✔

Task 3

(a)

Payment method	Immediate	Later date
Faster payment	✔	
Debit card		✔

(b)

Description	Difference
A cheque from a customer, which was entered in the cash book and paid into the bank last week, has been returned	Unpaid cheques
Cheques to suppliers have been recorded in the cash book, but are not yet shown on the bank statement	Unpresented cheques
The monthly payment for business rates has been made automatically by the ban	Direct debit
Cash and cheques from customers were recorded in the cash book and paid into the bank today, but are not yet shown on the bank statement	Outstanding lodgements

(c)

Adjustment	Cash book	Bank reconciliation
Bank charges are deducted on the bank statement	✔	
Cash sales recorded in the cash book are not shown on the bank statement		✔

Task 4

Cash book	Debit	Credit
	£	£
Closing balance b/d		947
Adjustments:		
GTK Ltd	349	
Bank charges		148
Adjusted balance c/d	746	

Bank reconciliation	£
Closing bank statement balance	652
Less unpresented cheques:	
Bridge Tools	607
Tenon Ltd	1,505
Add outstanding lodgements:	
Barber & Bates	469
Jackson & Co	245
Adjusted closing cash book balance	(746)

Task 5

(a)

1 January 20-6	Journal number: 001	
Account name	**Debit** **£**	**Credit** **£**
Cash	320	
Bank		585
Inventory	3,250	
Shop fittings	2,650	
Payables		1,050
Capital		4,585
Totals	6,220	6,220

(b) £ | 2,328

(c)

30 April 20-8	Journal number: 75	
Account name	**Debit** **£**	**Credit** **£**
Wages expense	8,320	
HMRC – Income tax		760
HMRC – NIC		970
Net wages		6,590
Totals	8,320	8,320

Task 6

(a)

Statement	Type of error
Tom has paid for repairs to his delivery van. He has coded the cost to his vehicles account	Error of principle
Alice has coded rent paid on her business premises to her stationery account	Error of commission
Daisy has bought copy paper for use in the office and paid in cash. She has forgotten to record the entry in her accounting system	Error of omission
Ernesto has bought a computer for his business. He has coded it as a debit to bank account and a credit to office equipment account	Reversal of entries

(b) **(i)**

Account name	Debit £	Credit £
Suspense		1,445

(ii)

Account name	Original balance £	New balance £	Debit in trial balance	Credit in trial balance
Office stationery	3,027	3,382	✔	
Rent received	8,040	9,840		✔
Delivery expenses	1,285	1,735	✔	
Bank (overdraft)	3,261	3,711		✔

(c)

Debit suspense account £125; credit purchases account £125	
Debit purchases account £250; credit suspense account £250	
Debit purchases account £125; credit suspense account £125	✔
Debit purchases account £125	

Task 7

(a)

Office equipment						
20-8	**Details**	**£**	**20-8**	**Details**		**£**
1 Dec	Balance b/d	22,250.00				
10 Dec	Bank	1,700.00				
			31 Dec	Balance c/d		23,950.00

Purchases returns						
20-8	**Details**	**£**	**20-8**	**Details**		**£**
			1 Dec	Balance b/d		358.26
			15 Dec	Payables ledger control		176.52
31 Dec	Balance c/d	534.78				

Receivables ledger control						
20-8	**Details**	**£**	**20-8**	**Details**		**£**
1 Dec	Balance b/d	12,582.36	10 Dec	Irrecoverable debt		146.29
31 Dec	Sales	7,054.18	31 Dec	Sales returns		278.84
			31 Dec	Bank		7,052.13
			31 Dec	Balance c/d		12,159.28

Capital						
20-8	**Details**	**£**	**20-8**	**Details**		**£**
31 Dec	Bank	1,890.50	1 Dec	Balance b/d		36,200.00
31 Dec	Balance c/d	34,309.50				

(b)

Item	Debit £	Credit £
Sales		120,452.18
Purchases	86,422.76	
Purchases returns		534.78
Bank	40,581.18	
Irrecoverable debts	480.29	
Capital		34,309.50
Office equipment	23,950.00	
Payables ledger control		7,054.92
Receivables ledger control	12,159.28	
VAT		1,242.13
Totals	163,593.51	163,593.51

Task 8

Item	Debit £	Credit £
Sales		42,580.31
Purchases	39,107.38	
Irrecoverable debts	515.59	
Bank	9,332.66	
Receivables ledger control	14,760.84	
Payables ledger control		10,108.76
Capital		14,092.36
Wages	3,064.96	
Totals	66,781.43	66,781.43

for your notes

for your notes

for your notes

for your notes

for your notes

for your notes

for your notes

for your notes

for your notes

for your notes

for your notes

for your notes